PROBLEMS AND PERSPECTIVES IN HISTORY

EDITOR: H. F. KEARNEY M.A. PH.D.

Origins of the
Scientific Revolution

PROBLEMS AND PERSPECTIVES IN HISTORY

EDITOR: H. F. KEARNEY M.A. PH.D.

Titles already published:

In Active Preparation:

Origins of the
Scientific Revolution

Hugh Kearney M.A. Ph.D.

READER IN HISTORY
UNIVERSITY OF SUSSEX

BARNES & NOBLE, Inc.
NEW YORK
PUBLISHERS & BOOKSELLERS SINCE 1873

PUBLISHED IN THE UNITED STATES IN 1967
BY BARNES & NOBLE, INC.
105 FIFTH AVENUE, NEW YORK

© HUGH KEARNEY 1964
FIRST PUBLISHED 1964

PRINTED IN GREAT BRITAIN BY
COX & WYMAN LTD, LONDON
FAKENHAM AND READING

TO THE UNIVERSITY OF SUSSEX

Contents

Foreword

'Study problems in preference to periods' was the excellent advice given by Lord Acton in his inaugural lecture at Cambridge. To accept it is one thing, to put it into practice is another. In fact, in both schools and universities the teaching of history, in depth, is often hindered by certain difficulties of a technical nature, chiefly to do with the availability of sources. In this respect, history tends to be badly off in comparison with literature or the sciences. The historical equivalents of set texts, readings, or experiments, in which the student is encouraged to use his own mind, are the so-called 'special periods'. If these are to be fruitful, the student must be encouraged to deal in his own way with the problems raised by historical documents and the historiography of the issues in question and he must be made aware of the wider perspectives of history. Thus, if the enclosure movement of the sixteenth century is studied, the student might examine the historiographical explanations stretching from More's *Utopia* and Cobbett to Beresford's *Lost Villages of England*. At the same time he might also be dealing with selected documents raising important problems. Finally he might be encouraged to realize the problems of peasantries at other periods of time, including Russia and China in the nineteenth and twentieth centuries. In this particular instance, thanks to Tawney and Power, *Tudor Economic Documents*, the history teacher is comparatively well off. For other special periods the situation is much more difficult. If, however, the study of history is to encourage the development of the critical faculties as well as the memory, this approach offers the best hope. The object of this series is to go some way towards meeting these difficulties.

The general plan of each volume in the series will be similar, with a threefold approach from aspects of historiography, documents, and editorial consideration of wider issues, though the structure and balance between the three aspects may vary.

A broad view is being taken of the limits of history. Political history will not be excluded, but considerable emphasis will be placed on economic, intellectual and social history. This approach owes a good deal to the outlook of a group of dons at the university of Sussex.

H. KEARNEY

Acknowledgements

We are grateful to the following for permission to include copyright material:

George Allen & Unwin Ltd., for material from *Mathematics in Western Culture* by M. Kline; the author and the Graduates Association of the National University of Ireland for material from 'Renaissance Art and Modern Science' by H. Butterfield in *University Review*; the Governors of Christ's Hospital for letter 452 from Newton to Hawes in Volume III of *Correspondence of Isaac Newton*, Ed. G. H. Turnbull; Columbia University Press for material from *The Career of Philosophy* by J. H. Randall, New York 1962, pp. 211–212 and from 'Francis Bacon – A Critical View' and 'Were the Scientific Academies Unscientific?' in *A History of Magic and Experimental Science* by L. Thorndike, New York 1958, Volumes VII and VIII; Doubleday & Company, Inc., Publishers for material from *Discoveries and Opinions of Galileo*, translated by Stillman Drake, Copyright (c) 1957 by Stillman Drake; the *Journal of the History of Ideas* for material from 'Mathematics and the Practical World' by F. R. Johnson and from 'Aristotelianism in Renaissance Italy' by J. H. Randall; the Library of King's College, Cambridge for letter 254 by Isaac Newton in Volume II of *Correspondence of Isaac Newton*, Ed. G. H. Turnbull; Lawrence & Wishart Ltd. for a letter of Engels to Starkenburg, 1894, in Volume II of *Selected Works of Marx and Engels*; the author, the Editor of *Annals of Science* and Taylor and Francis Ltd. for material from 'The Scientific Revolution and the Protestant Reformation' by Dr. S. F. Mason, printed in *Annals of Science* 1943; Princeton University Press for material from *The Aim and Structure of Physical Theory* by P. Duhem; the University of Chicago Press for material from 'The Sociological Roots of Science' by E. Zilsel in the *American Journal of Sociology* 1941–42, and the Regents of the University of Wisconsin for material from 'The Scholar and the Craftsman' by R. Hall in *Critical Problems in the History of Science*, Ed. Marshall Clagett, 1959, the University of Wisconsin Press, and from *The Science of Mechanics in the Middle Ages* by Marshall Clagett, 1959, the University of Wisconsin Press.

Introduction

If we believe in the existence of specifically modern attitudes to the world, distinct in quality from those held by men at earlier periods, the elements which go to the making of 'modernity' may be seen to make their first historical appearance in the sixteenth and seventeenth centuries. Some historians attributed the change to the liberation of men's minds during the Renaissance and the Reformation. Today, many historians would be more likely to stress the conservatism of these two movements rather than their radicalism. Their emphasis tends instead to fall on the effects of the change in men's attitude to the universe, which has been summed up in the phrase 'the Scientific Revolution'.

By this is meant above all the imaginative achievement associated with the names of Copernicus, Galileo and Newton. In the mid-sixteenth century, Copernicus took the first dramatic step of putting forward the hypothesis that the sun was the centre of the universe and working out mathematically the simplification which resulted. In the early seventeenth century, Galileo popularized the Copernican view and added his own contribution in another field by a mathematical demonstration of the laws which governed the speed of a falling body and the path of a projectile. By the end of the century Newton was able to show that the same forces which applied to falling bodies and projectiles also affected the motion of the planets. Within the space of a century and a half a revolution had occurred in the way in which men regarded the universe. Most of this was made possible by the application of mathematics to the problems of the natural world. The old-world picture had made some use of mathematics, especially in the field of astronomy, but in the main it had rested upon inspired commonsense observation. The new-world picture worked far more with mathematical abstractions, upon which general laws were erected. The result was that mathematics in 1700 enjoyed the prestige which in 1400 had been held by Aristotelian logic and philosophy. The fashionable philosophy of the day, Cartesianism, took mathematics as the model for its method and in other fields also mathematical techniques were applied.

All this is by now well known and though many of the details of the picture are still to be worked out, the scientific outline is clear enough. What is not clear is how it all came about. The actual statement of Galileo's equation governing falling bodies is comparatively simple. The real difficulty lies in discovering how his discovery was possible in Western Europe at this particular time. This is the historical problem which histories of science written by scientists have tended to ignore. Yet if we look at Western Europe against the background of the history of the world, the problem is immediately raised as to why one particular continent was able to make a contribution of this kind.

At the present time, three ways may be distinguished in which historians approach this. For some, the role of individual genius is the decisive factor; for others, the evolutionary character of scientific development requires emphasis; others, finally, stress the importance of the immediate social background. Few as yet have dealt with the Scientific Revolution against the background of world history. Needham, in his monumental work on Chinese science, is very much the exception. It would be easy to exaggerate the differences between these schools of thought. All agree, for example, in recognizing the importance of the insight which is called genius; where they differ is in the varying significance which they attach to it.

For men such as A. N. Whitehead and Herbert Butterfield, who emphasize the role of genius most strongly, the Renaissance still remains in many ways the decisive analogy by which to interpret the origins of the Scientific Revolution. It is of course true that both Whitehead and Butterfield go out of their way to treat the Middle Ages sympathetically. Whitehead maintained that without the long training of logical thought which Europe had received during the Middle Ages, modern science would have been impossible. Butterfield devoted a chapter of his book *The Origins of Modern Science* to appraising the significance of medieval dynamics. But for both the sixteenth and seventeenth centuries are pre-eminent. Whitehead describes the seventeenth as the 'century of Genius'. Butterfield uses phrases like 'an epic adventure' and 'a great episode in human experience'. In their explanation, the Scientific Revolution seems to have taken the place of the Renaissance, but it is essentially a movement of the same kind, one in which the imaginative leaps of particular individuals are more important than any social or economic trend.

Many other historians of science share this interpretation, though with differences of emphasis. Alexander Koyré, for example, concentrated his attention upon the personal achievement of Galileo. Giorgio di Santillana argued that the modern conception of space, which was essential to scientific advance, derived largely from the novel perspective of the Renaissance artist, especially Brunnelleschi. Arthur Koestler, in his much praised and much criticized book *The Sleepwalkers*, dealt with Copernicus, Kepler and Galileo from a point of view which suggested that accident as much as design led them to their great moments of discovery. We must repeat that the emphasis of such historians upon the genius of Galileo or Newton need not preclude a just appreciation of the achievement of the Middle Ages or of the significance of social factors. Antitheses, like entities, should not be multiplied. But, in general, they all would seem to agree with Karl Popper's judgement:

> We can never make sure that the right man will be attracted by scientific research. Nor can we make sure that there will be men of imagination who have the knack of investigating new hypotheses. And ultimately much depends on sheer luck . . . The human or personal factor will remain the irrational element in most or all institutional social theories.

A somewhat different point of view is to be found in the work of historians such as Clagett, Crombie and Maier. These may be said to take their starting point from the work of Pierre Duhem who regarded the writings of certain fourteenth-century Paris logicians as the critical step in the rise of modern science. Looked at in this way, the history of science takes on a more evolutionary character, and Galileo and his fellows do not appear as the absolute pioneers which they declared themselves to be. If it is true that a scientific tradition existed from the fourteenth century, then the task of 'putting on a new thinking cap' in the seventeenth was much less of a revolutionary achievement. This interpretation has not lacked support in recent years and has indeed received striking reinforcement thanks to the publication of M. Clagett *The Science of Mechanics in the Middle Ages*, E. J. Dijksterhuis *The Mechanisation of the World Picture* and J. H. Randall *The Career of Philosophy*. All of these criticize what they regard as the stereotyped view, in which Galileo emerges as an angel of light after centuries of obscurantism.

In contrast to all this, a good deal of recent work has hinged upon an examination of the nature of seventeenth-century society, in the hope of finding a clue about the origins of the Scientific Revolution. Following the lead given by Weber, some scholars, notably R. K. Merton and R. Hooykaas, have stressed the importance of the Reformation. On this view, religious experience and scientific experiment are thought to be interrelated. Others have emphasized specific social factors. Edgar Zilsel found the key to the rise of science in the alliance between the intellectual worker and the artisan, a conjunction which was possible only towards the end of the sixteenth century

Finally, Marxist historians have applied the materialist conception of history to the Scientific Revolution. Here, the decisive factor is seen to reside in the economic substructure. Economic activity gives rise to technological advance which in its turn provides the basis for theoretical progress. This chronological sequence is also a logical one from the Marxist point of view. Some allowance must be made for great men in science, as in politics, but their individual role is never indispensable. If they had not existed, their place would always have been filled by the operation of the laws of the historical process. Another Galileo would have arisen just as would another Napoleon.

In all these interpretations, the reaction of historians to the figure of Francis Bacon is very illuminating to their general attitude. For a mathematically minded historian such as Alexander Koyré, Francis Bacon is something of a bad joke in the history of science, a man inflated beyond measure. In contrast, Bacon appeals to those historians, including the Marxists, who regard scientific discovery as being linked in some way with the existing state of technical knowledge. Bacon is also of interest because he raises the question of nationalism, which may distort the history of science as much as it does political history. For any historian concerned to stress the English contribution to science, Bacon and that Baconian-inspired institution, the Royal Society, are of crucial significance. French historians or American historians may well take up an attitude entirely different. Finally, Bacon's own interpretation of his significance cannot be left out of account. If we accept his own assessment of his importance, we break one of the first rules of historical method. Yet this is what one is tempted to do under the spell of Bacon's prose. If he had not been capable of writing great prose, we may wonder whether he would have occupied so high a place in English accounts of the history of science.

At this point the reader may well feel that one interpretation is as good as another. At a particular stage of our knowledge this judgement may be quite true. In the absence of compelling evidence as to the truth or falsity of the wave theory of light, scientists have not felt embarrassed at the existence of two equally illuminating theories. Nor need the historian, provided he considers the evidence to be equally compelling all round or at least not sufficiently strong to compel belief one way or the other. It may well be that all these different interpretations contain a good deal of truth, that is to say, they are valid inferences from a reasonably representative body of evidence. What would be unhistorical would be to claim a monopoly of truth for one of them.

At this point it may be as well to indicate that there were limits to the scope of 'The Scientific Revolution'. There was loss and gain for example in the revival of Platonism during the Renaissance. It led on the one hand to the aery fantasies of Pico della Mirandola, on the other to the detachment of Galileo. For some historians, the Renaissance appears to be a mixed blessing. Even by 1700 there were vast areas of phenomena which remained untouched by fruitful scientific method and the dabbling of scientific amateurs with these lent substance to the charges of satirists such as Swift. In short, while it is important to realize the significance of the Scientific Revolution, it is equally important to realize that it had its limitations, which were exposed in due course.

By way of conclusion we may say that the same laws of historical evidence apply to the history of science as to the history of parliament or the history of France. What is distinctive is the different nature of the technical expertise, which is necessary to make an original contribution to knowledge in these fields. In some branches, though not all, of the history of science, a knowledge of mathematics is as essential to the student as a knowledge of Latin is to the medievalist. But the need for technical ability of this kind need not disguise the fact that ultimately the history of science is no more and no less scientific than constitutional or economic history.

Part One
PROBLEMS OF HISTORIOGRAPHY

I

The Renaissance

It has been argued from at least 1860, when Burckhardt published his Civilisation of the Renaissance, *that the Renaissance of the fifteenth century was not merely a revival of classical studies but also a renewal of the close and painstaking study of nature. The name of Leonardo da Vinci has been frequently cited in this connection. But Santillana (see M. Clagett, ed.* Critical Problems in the History of Science) *put forward the view that the Renaissance architect Brunelleschi was the real revolutionary, so far as science is concerned. According to this view the spatial world of the seventeenth century had its origins in the new departures in perspective, which came about as a result of the work of Brunelleschi. Santillana's emphasis is poles apart from that of scholars like Randall (see p. 51) who regard the logic schools of the Italian universities as the forcing house of novelty. On the other hand, Santillana's view is not far from that of Koyré, for whom the Platonic tradition was the decisive factor. If we follow this line of thought the Platonism of the studio and the study may be seen as not far removed from one another. Butterfield's view as expressed here is that the Renaissance witnessed an upsurge of ability which was 'scientific' in a pre-scientific age. The elements of the Scientific Revolution were present, so to speak, in solution.*

1 Renaissance Art and Modern Science

H. BUTTERFIELD

I

It is difficult to discover why in certain places and periods – in the Italy of the Renaissance, in the Golden Age of Spain and in Elizabethan England, for example – the student of history sees an unusually lavish blossoming of genius. It is equally difficult to account for the fact that in fifteenth-century Italy such a great wealth of genius and such a vast

3

array of minor talent should have come to be directed into the visual arts. In this latter case we are presented with a world in which the imposing personalities, the giants of the intellect, the men who tower like prophets, are people whom we associate primarily with painting, sculpture and architecture.

Possibly, in the absence of any great religious fervour, the Church and its academic institutions at this stage in man's intellectual history were felt as a constriction, so that the realm of theory and doctrine failed to offer the highest adventure to the mind. We today cannot easily enter into the experience of men who recognized – and rightly recognized – that the ancient world was still their superior; so that they saw no progress save in climbing back to the peaks which the ancients had conquered – no advance save by going farther than the Middle Ages had done in subservience to classical thought. When the greatest work of the pioneer was to be achieved through the further discovery of the writings of antiquity, the finder, the transcriber, the translator and the critic of new manuscripts held the key positions; so that for a moment Philology was indeed the Queen of the Sciences. For the actual theory of nature and the elucidation of its phenomena – for the explanation of the movements of the stars or the working of the human body – men still had no choice but to refer to those elaborate systems of thought which had been handed down to them from ancient Greece and Rome. The mind might be able to play a little along the margins of these complicated intellectual constructions; but the world at this time could not know how to begin producing a whole new system of scientific explanation. Famous historians of science have found the fifteenth century unoriginal, and have even seen it as a pause in the march of civilization itself.

Where it was a question of making things or of doing things, however, the men of that time seem to have found it possible to ride their ingenuity without fears or constrictions. General stagnation may exist in what we should call the natural sciences – in the work of explaining the physical operations of the universe – while technical invention, mining and metallurgy are moving ahead. The Copernican system was to have a more easy course as a help to astronomical calculation than as a statement of what actually happens in the skies. It is not strange, therefore, if in the visual arts in the fifteenth century there were openings for originality – for unfettered flight – which neither the conscious programme nor the limiting conditions of the Humanist movement would have allowed to individual minds. Geographical discovery, technical advance and artistic progress can occur in a world in which the philosopher and the natural scientist are inhibited and constrained.

It seems to be the case that there was less actual copying from ancient art during the Renaissance than students of this period were once inclined to imagine. And what was available was often Roman art of a decadent era, so that a too slavish imitation might have done harm – the Renaissance artist would have had little glory if he had not improved on his models. It was primarily amongst the artists in fact that there occurred a remarkable degree of liberation from the ancient world as well as from the Middle Ages. It was from the artists that the cry went up against tradition and authority and mere bookishness – the call for a kind of knowledge that should be based on direct observation and first-hand experience.

If by 'Renaissance' we mean not a closer subservience to the ancient classics but rather the recapture of the spirit that lay behind the achievements of antiquity – if what we have in mind in our use of the term is not merely the recovery of ancient learning but a release of creative forces – it will always be appropriate for us to take the line that such a Renaissance was occurring in fifteenth-century Florence in the realm of the visual arts. It had found its precursor in Giotto, who had worked in Florence in the first half of the fourteenth century; though in the latter half of that century the conservative Siena had held the supremacy in painting. Pisa had enjoyed the predominance in sculpture, and the style of the Renaissance had not yet evolved. There are more precursors, but the victory of Lorenzo Ghiberti in the competition over the Baptistery doors in 1401 serves to signalize the opening of a new era in Florence – this at a time when painting had not yet come to occupy a leading place in the story. Brunelleschi, who was closely contemporary with Ghiberti, is one of the heralds of that new era; he resurrected classical forms in architecture, but did so with a certain delicacy – loving open spaces, slim pillars, light arcades and slender mouldings. Leon Battista Alberti, who was a quarter of a century younger, also set out to recover ancient architectural forms; and he, similarly, combined them with a style of his own, producing buildings that were more heavily classical, buildings that tended to stress mass rather than line, so that with him 'solid walls come into their own'. Through both these men architecture was to exercise a remarkable influence on the art of painting in the fifteenth century – on the use of perspective, the conception of space, and the general composition of a picture. Through Donatello, whose age came well between that of these two men, and who also had found inspiration in the study of antiquity, it would seem that sculpture was to affect the painter's art in a parallel way, especially in that it encouraged the attempt to reproduce figures in the round.

Ghiberti, Brunelleschi, Donatello and the much younger Alberti – these are the circle of people whose activity in Florence prepared the way for the fifteenth-century developments. And with them – almost as young as Alberti – must be grouped Masaccio, one of the most remarkable of the painters of the century, who died under the age of thirty in 1428. He had just completed his work on the famous Brancacci frescoes – an achievement of unusual historical importance, once described as 'the training-school of Florentine painters'. Besides his originality in lighting a whole picture from a given angle, and graduating his colours to depict a receding landscape, Masaccio acquired his remarkable influence from the fact that he resumed what Giotto had already begun – namely the task of giving painted figures a sculptural quality, depicting them as solid bodies standing in space, instead of presenting them flat on the canvas. So Vasari was able to say of him that he was the first artist to attain the imitation of things as they really are.

II

We are told that Masaccio learned geometry from Brunelleschi, who had been taught by Paolo Toscanelli, the greatest mathematician of his time. The whole movement had its doctrinal side; and Alberti (who dedicated one of his works to Toscanelli) completed in 1435 what has been described as 'the first treatise on the art of painting ever written'. Underlying all his theories, as Sir Kenneth Clark points out, is 'the assumption that painting is concerned with the accurate representation of the visible world'. In particular, objects were to be delineated in such a way as to make them 'appear in relief'. Heads, for example, should 'seem to stand out from the picture as if they were sculptured'. Granted that this was the object, it is perhaps not too great an abuse of the term to suggest that what is remarkable about the fifteenth-century Italians is the 'scientific' way in which they set about to accomplish their end. It is all the more remarkable if Sir Kenneth Clark is correct in his view that 'this scientific basis of renaissance naturalism was the one way in which the artists of the early renaissance believed that they might surpass antiquity'.

From Alberti, who says that 'no painter can paint well without a thorough knowledge of geometry', to Leonardo da Vinci, who opens his *Treatise on Painting* with the words 'Let no one who is not a mathematician read my work', the theorists of the artistic movement are particularly concerned to stress the importance of mathematics. The study was one which was relevant of course to the science of perspective and to any discussion of optical questions. It governed the treatment of the problem of proportion; and in those days the artist was greatly interested in measurements. Geometry assisted the painter in the work of composition, the establishment of the general lay-out of a picture. There even appears the view that in the mysticism of number the realms of beauty and of mathematics meet. In the case of some of the great Renaissance figures there can be no doubt that mathematics stood as something more than a mere instrument for the achieving of an artistic end.

Alberti writes:

> In painting the nude, begin with the bones, then add the muscles and then cover the figures with flesh in such a way as to leave the position of the muscles visible. It may be objected that a painter should not represent what cannot be seen, but this procedure is analogous to drawing a nude and then covering it with draperies.

The procedure, admirable as it may be, is not one which should be taken for granted at the beginning of the story: and Sir Kenneth Clark, in quoting this passage, tells us that when the treatise was written, painting offered no example of such nudes which had afterwards been covered with draperies.

The course of Florentine painting in the fifteenth century may owe something to great men who were more than painters and who sought to pierce the world of visible objects with the fire of a penetrating mind. Alberti wrote on many subjects: jurisprudence, shipbuilding, architecture and the training of horses, for example; he may be said to belong to both the arts and the sciences of the Humanist period. We often hear of the claim made in this period that art should be regarded as a branch of knowledge or a form of science; and this must have sprung from something more than a mere desire to assert its status in the world or to rescue it from the charge of being a mechanical pursuit. Alberti requires the artist to know geometry so as to be able to give a proper reproduction of what he sees. But when he expects the painter also to have a scientific understanding of the thing seen, he is pointing along a

7

path which might carry an artist far from home. The path is insidious, for there is always a terrible danger that men will become interested in the thing they have set themselves to study. They are so prone to lose sight of an ultimate objective, so inclined to bury themselves in what initially (or ostensibly) was only the means, and to turn this into an end-in-itself. This would be particularly true in the fifteenth century when frontiers were still blurred, and the role of the artist or the function of art had not been brought to its modern degree of specialization. The attempt to achieve realistic representation ought, perhaps, to be regarded as a quasi-scientific endeavour in any case.

Once launched on the quest for a more realistic representation of the visible world, Florentine painting distinguished itself by the specialized way in which it concentrated on the task. We must not say that it 'discovered' nature or the external universe; but it did achieve something new through the intentness and consistency with which it observed and analysed things for the purpose of naturalistic representation. It concentrated its attention particularly on the problems connected with figure-painting; and here on the one hand it sought to achieve the effect of solidity and relief, while on the other hand it set itself to convey the impression of movement. One thing which had to be achieved – the thing which could be achieved by dint of patient study – was a more accurate and detailed knowledge of the structure of the human body. Florence developed, therefore, a fervent study of anatomy.

By the middle of the fifteenth century the new movement had come to a significant stage. This is the period also when painting begins to hold the leading place amongst the arts. The predominant figures, Paolo Uccello, Andrea del Castagno and Domenico Veneziano, showed a particular interest in the scientific work that preceded artistic activity. With them may be mentioned Piero della Francesca, who worked elsewhere, but was the disciple and friend of Alberti, and has been called 'the true heir of the first Florentine renaissance'. Sometimes it might seem that for Uccello painting was merely the occasion for showing how the different problems of perspective could be solved. In his depiction of God in the Sacrifice of Noah, we are told, he 'seems to have been possessed with nothing except the scientific intention to find out how a man swooping down head foremost would have looked if at a given instant of his fall he had been suddenly congealed and suspended in space'. Not uncommonly do we learn from the critic (as in the case of St Jerome by Fra Lippo Lippi) that a painter has failed to turn his anatomical knowledge to artistic account, 'lapsing into a realm quite devoid of spiritual significance'. Piero della Francesca provides an impressive example of the way in which the theorist and the geometer may preside over the masterpieces of a great painter. He proved himself a genuine mathematician in his technical work on perspective, his treatise *De Quinque Corporibus Regolaribus* and his interest in the mysticism of number.

During the period between 1460 and 1490 Alesso Baldovinetti was a further example of the way in which the scientist might prevail over the painter. The two great masters of schools in Florence in this period – Antonio Pollajuolo and Andrea Verrocchio – distinguished themselves in the realm of study, particularly in the science of anatomy. Pollajuolo carried his work in this field farther than others did, studying the muscular system in particular, and showing his prowess in the depiction of violent action and vigorous movement. Perhaps he was the first of the artists to dissect corpses. Yet it was said of him that, through sheer absorption in anatomy, he was unable to set a single human being on his feet.

The scientific attitude to art would receive further countenance from the ease with which it could establish itself in the training of the studios. Its effects would be exaggerated by the competition in sheer dexterity which must tend to arise when the criterion of art lies in its realism. The multitude of mediocre painters who were enslaved to current fashions showed the dangers of the tendency in ways to which Leonardo da Vinci drew attention later. It was the greater men who would bring a strong artistic sense or a rich humanity or a fine emotion to dominate their specialized knowledge and acquired proficiency. In the paradoxical case of Botticelli we even find a man who was caught for a time in this movement of scientific realism though it went against his deeper nature. And the art critic, assessing the Florentines of the fifteenth century, often speaks of them as though he were estimating the successive contributions of scientists to the development of a science.

In one respect the whole movement carried painting away from Giotto and Masaccio, with whom the story began; and the influence of the two men, when it returned on occasion during the century, would come as something separate and super-imposed. The Florentines tended to forget the art of massive shapes and broad sweeps. The virtue of their art in general did not seem to lie in any grandeur of conception. They brought rather an intent concern for *minutiæ* – a remarkable meticulousness in the reproduction of those details which Masaccio had been prepared to sacrifice for the sake of the general effect. They were primarily draughtsmen – Pollajuolo, for example, amongst the greatest of them – and their studies of the visible world tended to be linear in character, their preoccupation tended to be the analytical one. The painters had often been trained in the craft of the goldsmith, and this must have encouraged them in their concern for points of minute detail. It was left for the Venetians, therefore, to explore the use of colour, which amongst the Florentines sometimes appeared almost as an afterthought.

The scientific naturalism of the fifteenth century may have had its origin in the thrusts and gropings of deeply inquiring minds. But it must have been congenial to the disposition of the Florentines, many of whom, as Berenson has noted, seemed to lean rather to the sciences than to the arts. Men whom we today would regard as scientific in their inclinations would have found it natural to become artists by profession in the Italy of the fifteenth century. For the 'natural scientist' did not exist as yet, and the teacher of natural philosophy in the schools was farther removed from the type than some of the artists and teachers in Florence. We need not be surprised to learn, therefore, that those who in another age would have flocked to the workshop of Galileo congregated during the fifteenth century in the studio of a great painter.

III

The process of secularization which was taking place in the city-states of Renaissance Italy is visible in the arts, which were advancing to a kind of autonomy. In many respects it is the figure of the modern 'artist' that now makes its appearance on the stage of history. In the first quarter of the fifteenth century the convents had still been significant centres of artistic production. Florentine life then became luxurious; magnificent palaces and houses were built; works of art in a myriad of forms had to be produced for their ornamentation. The courts and city councils of Italy, as well as churches and monasteries, had important commissions for the artists. The activity of these men came to have a public character; on occasion there would be a general holiday to celebrate the completion of a work. In the atmosphere of Renaissance Italy personal fame had a part to play. A leader of reputation would draw the apprentices to his studio. The rivalry between one painter and another might divide a city. The artist could even be temperamental, as though he were a person who must 'follow the law of his own being'. When the artist was a Leonardo da Vinci, the patron might find himself treated with extraordinary wilfulness. Michelangelo's father thought that his son had chosen a lowly career; but on occasion even a Pope had to coax and court and humour the great genius. So we are told that in Michelangelo the artist appears as a formidable prophet, in Raphael he lives as a cultivated lord, in Titian he becomes a grandee.

Yet the artist had not achieved anything like that specialization of function which we today might be tempted to impute to him. The studio was something of a workshop; if not rather a factory; and, as we have seen, many painters were trained initially in the goldsmith's craft. The artist prepared his own colours, experimented with his materials, and in many respects joined hands with the technician or the mechanic. Not only would the same man be painter, sculptor and architect; but he would also be what we should call the 'inventor' and the engineer. He was the scientific expert, consulted by courts which needed a spectacle for an entertainment, towns which needed water supply, and military leaders who called for the latest device in time of war. Giotto designed the fortifications of Florence in the early four-teenth century and Michelangelo renewed the work in 1529. Francesco di Giorgio Martini was in full charge of Siena's water supply in the 1470s. It is from him that we date modern speculation on the problem of defence against artillery. He constructed fortresses, insisting that the virtue of these should be sought 'in the artifice of their planning rather than the thickness of their walls'. He designed a tank, planned a torpedo-boat, suggested diving equipment, and gave his views on the arrangement of harbours. Like other Renaissance artists he interested himself in military mining, as in 1495, when he served the King of Naples against the French invader. His rival in the latter part of the fifteenth century was Giuliano di San Gallo, who also worked along with Raphael on the Church of St Peter's. His successor in the sixteenth century was Baldassare Peruzzi. Leonardo da Vinci came between the two.

It is perhaps legitimate, then, to envisage the art-history of the Renaissance in its aspect as a chapter in the history of science. We may ask whether the Florentine painter of the fifteenth century is not as much a parent of the modern scientist as was the natural philosopher in the schools. The fact that the artist studied nature in so direct and methodical a manner was itself not without significance in this con-nection. The leaf-carvings in cathedral sculpture in the latter Middle Ages are an evidence of the accuracy of the artist's eye. In the whole fifteenth-century movement that we have been examining, empirical observation was itself being carried to a higher power. The theory of nature as taught in the schools, and the practice of observation as taught in the studios, were in fact proceeding on parallel lines. They were not adjusted to one another as yet; they were in imperfect sympathy with one another – they did not even recognize one another – but they share the honour of being the precursors of modern science. Nobody could realize in the fifteenth century the peculiar way in which these separate things, when they were brought together, would each take the other in its grip. Nobody realized, as we do, that the observed data were going to bring about a radical change in the very structure of science. It is not always remembered to what an extent men, when they observe the world, see what the books prescribe, what contemporary science tells them to see, and what the painter may have taught them to look for. If we ourselves were confronted with a new system of scientific explanation (or with the need of one) we should then discover how difficult it is to unwind ourselves out of the old system and to uncoil the mind that it has shaped – how difficult it is to see the objects of the world other than in the terms of the inherited teaching. Even when trained sixteenth-century minds found that they could not trace the things that Galen had recorded, they were hesitant – they lacked the confidence to believe their own eyes. Alternatively, they would be prepared to argue that the body of a human being must have suffered a change since the time of Galen. There were inhibitions, therefore; but a primary stage in the development of the Scientific Revolution is the establishment of more accurate observation. And this – even in the realm of the scientist – follows hard on the tradition which the Florentine artists had set.

It can hardly be an accident that anatomy was the first of the sciences to be transformed at the beginning of modern times; and that the new stage was reached in this subject as the result of the establishment of more authentic observation. Possibly here, if not elsewhere, the artist was helped by the fact that he studied the subject unencumbered by some of the theory which prevailed in the medical schools. Leonardo da Vinci advanced the science though it would appear that he was himself hampered by the theories current in the scholarly world. Vesalius, who inaugurated the modern study of the subject, has been described as combining the power of the artist with the skill of the scientist. Another sixteenth-century anatomist, Fabricius, produced works in which the illustrations are the notable feature, since they exhibit far more details than the text. It has been said that they could be used in a modern textbook, and it would appear that the artist saw more than Fabricius himself was able to do. Men like Leonardo da Vinci and Albrecht Dürer produced pictures of plant and animal life so precise that it is not easy for the modern world to understand why the writers on natural history could be content to go on trafficking still with symbolism and fable.

From the time of the Renaissance, illustrations begin to play a remarkable part in the actual communication of scientific knowledge. The purely conventional and symbolical drawings which had sufficed for so long during the Middle Ages were supplanted by accurate detailed representation. Not only printing, but also certain devices that we associate with printing, such as woodcuts and copper-plate engraving, put new instruments at the disposal of the scientific teacher. If the scientist of modern times is a blend between the artist, the artisan and the natural philosopher, the Florentine painter of the fifteenth century is almost a trial combination of the various elements.

IV

Leonardo da Vinci seems to represent the climax of this piece of story. He combines the required ingredients though he may not possess them in the right admixture. In a way, he outranges the intellectual system of his time; so that only after the passage of centuries – only after the world has had to learn the lesson over again, so to speak, and has learned it this time in the slower way – do his dreams and premonitions, his hunches and hypotheses, come to rank as scientific truths. It is not easy to say what place in the scheme of history such a man must have – in what sense he is a freak and a sport, and in what sense an effective collaborator in the progress of science. He is the scientist doomed to be like a fish out of water, the scientist stranded in the pre-scientific age.

He had read Aristotle, Archimedes, Hippocrates, Celsus, Ptolemy, Vitruvius and Pliny amongst the ancients. In respect of the theory of nature he gained much guidance from medieval scholars, such as Albert of Saxony, Albert the Great and Nicholas of Cusa. Some of the surprising things in his notebooks have turned out to be transcripts or paraphrases from the later scholastic writers. It may still be found that more of his scientific utterances came from other men, for he was always ready to learn from books or to search the minds of his mathematical friends. He was no slave of classical teaching, and he was clearly not the man to cringe before any form of established authority. Neither in his art nor in his science did he set out to be an imitator of classical models. He tells us repeatedly that nature is the only mistress to pursue, that experience and experiment are the only paths to certainty. He knew that he was no man of letters, he said – that, therefore, he was open to attack from the presumptuous Humanists, the men who made books merely out of other books.

Even in his writing there is imaginative power – as when he tells of the mirror which goes forth proudly holding fast to the image of a queen which it has captured; or when he describes the effect of the sunshine on the waves 'which intersect like the scales of a fir cone'. Perhaps because he was in a certain sense born out of due time, he presents himself as a man in whom intellect and imagination seem to be straining at the leash. It is as though here was a modern scientist but as yet there was no modern science into which he could get himself geared. The precursor of Galileo would collect lizards, serpents and the like, in order to compound out of the various images a hideous monster that would terrify the beholder. He gives evidence of the qualities that seem to characterize the scientific inquirer (or of the aberrations to which he is subject) in days when physical science has not yet quite found its feet. He pursues his researches in a whole variety of fields at the same time, like a person too exhilarated by the discovery he has just made of a world which is a wonderland. And he loves any monstrosity in nature, is fascinated by the gigantic and the deformed, happy to gaze on complicated tangles or fantastic interweavings, and filled with child-like awe in the face of a mighty storm or a rampant battle-scene. It was his habit to indulge in pieces of mystification, to describe imaginary travels, to recount animal fables and 'to ruminate over the ruin of cities'. It is not certain whether some of his drafts and narrations, including the description of an earthquake which burned a town, are to be taken as evidence of an actual journey which the reader might be tempted to think that he made to Armenia at some period or other.

He nursed grandiose projects and could write that he had invented a machine which would take to the air and 'fill the world with its great fame'. Even in his painting his more ambitious undertakings often remained uncompleted, because he had set his mind on a perfection that he could not attain, or because there were times when he could not bring himself to continue a task till he was satisfied that he knew the reasons for things. New projects would make him tire of the old ones; and a man who was with him in 1501 wrote that at this period he was working hard at geometry and in the highest degree of impatience at the idea of painting. 'His mathematical experiments have drawn him so far from painting that he cannot bear to hold the brush.'

On many occasions his scientific interests would appear to have been associated with his art. He had a critical interest, for example, in problems of light and shade. He would experiment in order to discover what objects look like when seen through a fine spray of water or a cloud of smoke. He injured his work on occasion because he liked to try out an experiment with the artist's materials. And just as there was knowledge of anatomy behind his figures, there would be geological observation behind his landscapes – not restricted in either case to superficialities, but reaching to a profound sense of structure. It is not clear whether it is the eye of the artist or the eye of the scientist which prevails when he describes or depicts the rush of water, the swirl of a stream, the meeting of rivers, the pattern of a whirlpool, the picture of interlacing branches or currents of air, and the passage of wind through a trumpet. Perhaps it was the sympathetic vision of the artist in him which realized that, when studying flight or the action of birds on the wing, it would be useful to follow the analogy of water, where the motions would be visible, and therefore to extend the inquiry to the case of swimming. The mind that loves to reproduce the path of birds in flight or the behaviour of swirling water seems to be the one that also seizes on the tumultuous curls, the windings and the folds, of an old man's beard, a woman's tresses or a ruffled cloak. Leonardo's first thought on the possibility of a human bird, with mechanically-operated wings, have been associated with the plan of a realistic portrait of Daedalus; alternatively, with the task of producing an ingenious spectacle for a theatrical entertainment. And certainly Leonardo's scientific interests blend naturally into his architectural studies when he examines the causes of fissures in walls, the laws governing arches, and the support or foundations that a building will require. It is clear, moreover, that his extraordinary power as a draughtsman contributed to the scientific value of his anatomical studies.

Where truth was to be reached by immediate observation (occasionally perhaps with hints or assistance from some ancient writer) he could quickly see the implications of a discovery. Even on some of these occasions, however, it is illuminating to learn how curiously he could go wrong. He knew the possibilities of steam as a form of power, but he suggested its application not to the locomotive but to projectiles, where it could hardly be so effective as the gunpowder already in use. He declared, before Copernicus, that the sun does not move around the earth; and he attacked the astrologers – attacked the whole idea that the heavenly bodies could have any effect on what was happening in the world. Even here, however, he carried the argument too far, and denied that the moon could have any influence over the tides.

He set himself to examine the curious problems – the obvious puzzles – that tax the ingenuity of the observer of nature when scientific interest is in its early stages. He asked how birds fly, what hail is, what is the nature of the flame of the candle, what is the distance of the sun from the earth, and why, when the moon is a crescent, one can still see the whole disc faintly illuminated. He showed that the age of a tree could be discovered by counting the number of concentric rings on the cross-section of its trunk. He would apply mathematical calculation to observed data, proving, for example, that the time necessary for the Po to have worn down its existing channel (supposing the time to be estimated from the visible effects of its present activity) must have been much longer than the Church allowed one to believe that the river had been in existence at all. Applying his mathematics, his ingenuity, his observation of shell-fish, and the accepted knowledge of the operations of the laws of nature, he was able to show that at the Flood the waters could never have risen ten cubits above the highest mountain in the world (so covering the whole globe) and then subsided after forty days, without either a miracle or an incredible evaporation. And he argued that the marine shells on the mountains of Italy could never have been carried so far in those forty days – indeed that the creatures were alive when they were deposited there, and that the plains of Italy had once been under the sea.

Along with this he had an extraordinary zeal in the application of knowledge to utilitarian purposes. He spent much of his life discussing hydraulic matters – pumps, fountains, locks, harbours, diving-suits, canals, and even the diversion of rivers. He dealt with problems relating to the science of war – artillery, fortresses, submarine attack, and the like. We are told that he foreshadowed not only aeroplanes but tanks, poison-gas, wireless telegraphy and submarines. He came nearest to an organized scheme of experiments in his studies of aviation; but the plan of these shows that he lived too early to see the essential features of the modern experimental method.

He thought that the ancients were wrong in trying to define the nature of the soul or of life itself – in seeking the kind of truth which it is impossible to fasten down with proofs and demonstrations. All this, he said, involved too great a neglect of the kind of truths which can be established by observation and experiment. His whole attitude to the physical universe, his feeling for the way in which it operates – his sense of the right approach to make to all its machinery for the purpose of understanding it – show that he was in advance of his time, his insight superior perhaps to that of Sir Francis Bacon, who lived a hundred years later. It is possible that behind the Scientific Revolution lies some subtle change in the quality of men's feeling for things – the kind of change which it will always be difficult for the historian to measure or to analyse. In an age of multiplying clocks and machines it may have been a tendency to approach the world with a greater disposition to ask merely 'how things worked'. It may have been a change in men's feeling for matter. A time arrives, for example, when clearly men fall unawares into the assumption that the stars cannot possibly be composed of a kind of material which has no weight. It is not clear whether such changes in sensibility would be associated with the habit of handling things in workshop and studio.

Leonardo was not without influence on his successors; but, even in his scientific achievements, he stands, curiously enough, more like an artist in the history of art than a scientist linked to a chain of scientific progress. Even now the heritage from the ancient world was hardly completed and was insufficiently digested. The basic scientific instruments were not to make their appearance until the seventeenth century. In any case it was possible that a flood of development was bound to be blocked until some Galileo settled the principle of inertia and some Harvey established the circulation of the blood. Bacon was to claim later that the introduction of a more satisfactory method would some day put the work of discovery within the reach of men without great intellect. Leonardo, on the other hand, shows that genius itself may meet frustration in science if it flounders in a pre-scientific age.

University Review
vol. i, no. 2, 1954, pp. 25–37

2 Painting and Perspective

M. KLINE

The world's the book where the eternal sense
  Wrote his own thoughts; the living temple where,
  Painting his very self, with figures fair
  He filled the whole immense circumference.

T. CAMPANELLA

During the Middle Ages painting, serving somewhat as the hand-maiden of the Church, concentrated on embellishing the thoughts and doctrines of Christianity. Towards the end of this period, the painters, along with other thinkers in Europe, began to be interested in the natural world. Inspired by the new emphasis on man and the universe about him the Renaissance artist dared to confront nature, to study her deeply and searchingly, and to depict her realistically. The painters revived the glory and gladness of an alive world and reproduced beautiful forms which attested to the delightfulness of physical exist-ence, the inalienable right to satisfy natural wants, and the pleasures afforded by earth, sea and air.

For several reasons the problem of depicting the real world led the Renaissance painters to mathematics. The first reason was one that could be operative in any age in which the artist seeks to paint realistic-ally. Stripped of colour and substance the objects that painters put on canvas are geometrical bodies located in space. The language for dealing with these idealized objects, the properties they possess as idealizations, and the exact relationships that describe their relative locations in space are all incorporated in Euclidean geometry. The artists need only avail themselves of it.

The Renaissance artist turned to mathematics not only because he sought to reproduce nature but also because he was influenced by the revived philosophy of the Greeks. He became thoroughly familiar and imbued with the doctrine that mathematics is the essence of the real world, that the universe is ordered and explicable rationally in terms of geometry. Hence, like the Greek philosopher, he believed that to penetrate to the underlying significance, that is, the reality of the theme that he sought to display on canvas, he must reduce it to its mathematical content. Very interesting evidence of the artist's attempt to discover the mathematical essence of his subject is found in one of

Leonardo's studies in proportion. In it he tried to fit the structure of the ideal man to the ideal figures, the square and circle.

The sheer utility of mathematics for accurate description and the philosophy that mathematics is the essence of reality are only two of the reasons why the Renaissance artist sought to use mathematics. There was another reason. The artist of the late medieval period and the Renaissance was, also, the architect and engineer of his day and so was necessarily mathematically inclined. Businessmen, secular princes, and ecclesiastical officials assigned all construction problems to the artist. He designed and built churches, hospitals, palaces, cloisters, bridges, fortresses, dams, canals, town walls, and instruments of warfare. Numerous drawings of such engineering projects are in da Vinci's notebooks and he, himself, in offering his services to Lodovico Sforza, ruler of Milan, promised to serve as an engineer, constructor of military works, and designer of war machines, as well as architect, sculptor, and painter. The artist was even expected to solve problems involving the motion of cannon balls in artillery fire, a task which in those times called for profound mathematical knowledge. It is no exaggeration to state that the Renaissance artist was the best practising mathematician and that in the fifteenth century he was also the most learned and accomplished theoretical mathematician.

The specific problem which engaged the mathematical talents of the Renaissance painters and with which we shall be concerned here was that of depicting realistically three-dimensional scenes on canvas. The artists solved this problem by creating a totally new system of mathematical perspective and consequently refashioned the entire style of painting.

The various schemes employed throughout the history of painting for organizing subjects on plaster and canvas, that is, the various systems of perspective, can be divided into two major classes, conceptual and optical. A conceptual system undertakes to organize the persons and objects in accordance with some doctrine or principle that has little or nothing to do with the actual appearance of the scene itself. For example, Egyptian painting and relief work were largely conceptual. The sizes of people were often ordered in relation to their importance in the politico-religious hierarchy. Pharaoh was usually the most important person and so was the largest. His wife would be next in size and his servants even smaller. Profile views and frontal views were used simultaneously even for different parts of the same figure. In order to indicate a series of people or animals one behind the other, the same figure was repeated slightly displaced. Modern painting, as well as most Japanese and Chinese painting, is also conceptual.

An optical system of perspective, on the other hand, attempts to convey the same impression to the eye as would the scene itself. Although Greek and Roman painting was primarily optical, the influence of Christian mysticism turned artists back to a conceptual system, which prevailed throughout the Middle Ages. The early Christian and medieval artists were content to paint in symbolic terms, that is, their settings and subjects were intended to illustrate religious themes and induce religious feelings rather than to represent real people in the actual and present world. The people and objects were highly stylized and drawn as though they existed in a flat, two-dimensional vacuum. Figures that should be behind one another were usually alongside or above. Stiff draperies and angular attitudes were characteristic. The backgrounds of the paintings were almost always of a solid colour, usually gold, as if to emphasize that the subjects had no connection with the real world.

The early Christian mosaic 'Abraham with Angels', a typical example of the Byzantine influence, illustrates the disintegration of ancient perspective. The background is essentially neutral. The earth, tree, and bushes are artificial and lifeless, the tree being shaped peculiarly to fit the border of the picture. There is no foreground or base on which the figures and objects stand. The figures are not related to each other and, of course, spatial relations are ignored because measures and sizes were deemed unimportant. The little unity there is in the picture is supplied by the gold background and the colour of the objects.

Though remnants of an optical system used by the Romans were sometimes present in medieval painting, this Byzantine style predominated. An excellent example, indeed one that is regarded as the flower of medieval painting, is 'The Annunciation' by Simone Martini (1285–1344). The background is gold. There is no indication of visual perception. The movement in the painting is from the angel to the Virgin and then back to the angel. Though there is loveliness of colour, surface, and sinuous line, the figures themselves are unemotional and arouse no emotional response in the onlooker. The effect of the whole is mosaic-like. Perhaps the only respect in which this painting makes any advance towards realism is in its use of a ground plane or floor on which objects and figures rest and which is distinct from the gilt background.

Characteristic Renaissance influences which steered the artists towards realism and mathematics began to be felt near the end of the thirteenth century, the century in which Aristotle became widely known by means of translations from the Arabic and the Greek. The painters became aware of the lifelessness and unreality of medieval painting and consciously sought to modify it. Efforts towards naturalism appeared in the use of real people as subjects of religious themes, in the deliberate use of straight lines, multiple surfaces, and simple forms of geometry, in experiments with unorthodox positions of the figures, in attempts to render emotions, and in the depiction of drapery falling and folding round parts of bodies as it actually does rather than in the flat folds of the conventional medieval style.

The essential difference between medieval and Renaissance art is the introduction of the third dimension, that is, the rendering of space, distance, volume, mass, and visual effects. The incorporation of three-dimensionality could be achieved only by an optical system of representation, and conscious efforts in this direction were made by Duccio (1255–1319) and Giotto (1267–1336), at the beginning of the fourteenth century. Several devices appeared in their works that are at least worth noticing as stages in the development of a mathematical system. Duccio's 'Madonna in Majesty' has several interesting features. The composition, first of all, is severely simple and symmetrical. The lines of the throne are made to converge in pairs and thus suggest depth. The figures on either side of the throne are presumably standing on one level but they are painted one above the other in several layers. This manner of depicting depth is known as terraced perspective, a device very common in the fourteenth century. The drapery is somewhat natural as exemplified by the folds over the Madonna's knee. Also there is some feeling for solidity and space and some emotion in the faces. The picture as a whole still contains much of the Byzantine tradition. There is a liberal use of gold in the background and in the details. The pattern is still mosaic-like. Because the throne is not properly foreshortened to suggest depth, the Madonna does not appear to be sitting on it.

Even more significant is Duccio's 'The Last Supper'. The scene is a partially boxed-in room, a background very commonly used during the fourteenth century and one that marks the transition from interior to exterior scenes. The receding walls and receding lines, somewhat foreshortened, suggest depth. The parts of the room fit together. Several details about the treatment of the ceiling are important. The lines of the middle portion come together in one area, which is called the vanishing area for a reason that will be made clear later. This technique was consciously used by many painters of the period as a device to portray depth. Second, lines from each of the two end-sections of the ceiling, which are symmetrically located with respect to the centre, meet in pairs at points which lie on one vertical line. This scheme, too, known as vertical or axial perspective, was widely used to achieve depth. Neither scheme was used systematically by Duccio but both were developed and applied by later painters of the fourteenth century. Suggestions of the real world, such as the bushes on the left side of the painting, should be noticed.

Unfortunately, Duccio did not treat the whole scene in 'The Last Supper' from a single point of view. The lines of the table's edges approach the spectator, contrary to the way in which the eye would see them. The table appears to be higher in the back than in the front and the objects on the table do not seem to be lying flat on it. In fact they project too far into the foreground. Nevertheless, there is a sense of realism particularly in regard to the larger features of the painting.

It can be said that three-dimensionality is definitely present in Duccio's work. The figures have mass and volume and are related to each other and to the composition as a whole. Lines are used in accordance with some particular schemes, and planes are foreshortened. Light and shadow are also used to suggest volume.

The father of modern painting was Giotto. He painted with direct reference to visual perceptions and spatial relations and his results tended towards a photographic copy. His figures possessed mass, volume, and vitality. He chose homelike scenes, distributed his figures in a balanced arrangement, and grouped them in a manner agreeable to the eye.

One of Giotto's best paintings, 'The Death of St Francis', like Duccio's 'The Last Supper', employs the popular transitional device, a partially boxed-in room. The room does suggest a localized three-dimensional scene as opposed to a flat two-dimensional scene existing nowhere. The careful balance of the component objects and figures is clearly intended to appeal to the eye. Equally obvious are the relations of the figures to each other, though none is related to the background. In this painting and in others by Giotto, the portions of the rooms or buildings shown seem to stand on the ground. Foreshortening is employed to suggest depth.

Giotto is not usually consistent in his point of view. In his 'Salome's Dance', the two walls of the alcove on the right do not quite jibe with each other, nor do the table and ceiling of the dining-room. Nevertheless, the three-dimensionality of this painting can no longer be overlooked. Rather interesting and significant is the bit of architecture at the left. The real world is introduced even at the expense of irrelevance.

Giotto was a key figure in the development of optical perspective. Though his paintings are not visually correct and though he did not introduce any new principle, his work on the whole shows great improvement over that of his predecessors. He himself was aware of the advances he had made, for he often went to unnecessary lengths in order to display his skill. This is almost certainly the reason for the inclusion of the tower in his 'Salome's Dance'.

Advances in technique and principles may be credited to Ambrogio Lorenzetti (active 1323–48). He is noteworthy for the organization of his themes in realistic, localized areas; his lines are vigorous and his figures robust and humanized. Progress is evident in the 'Annunciation'. The ground plane on which the figures rest is now definite and clearly distinguished from the rear wall. The ground also serves as a measure of the sizes of the objects and suggests space extending back to the rear. A second major advance is that the lines of the floor which recede from the spectator meet at one point. Finally, the blocks are foreshortened more and more the farther they are in the background. On the whole Lorenzetti handled space and three-dimensionality as well as anyone in the fourteenth century. Like Duccio and Giotto he failed to unite all the elements in his paintings. In the 'Annunciation' the wall and floor are not related. Nevertheless, there is good intuitive, though not mathematical, handling of space and depth.

With Lorenzetti we reach the highest level attained by the Renaissance artists before the introduction of a mathematical system of perspective. The steps made thus far towards the development of a satisfactory optical system show how much the artists struggled with the problem. It is evident that these innovators were groping for an effective technique.

In the fifteenth century the artists finally realized that the problem of perspective must be studied scientifically and that geometry was the key to the problem. This realization may have been hastened by the study of ancient writings on perspective which had recently been exhumed along with Greek and Roman art. The new approach was, of course, motivated by far more than the desire to attain verisimilitude. The greater goal was understanding of the structure of space and discovery of some of the secrets of nature. This was an expression of the

Renaissance philosophy that mathematics was the most effective means of probing nature and the form in which the ultimate truths would be phrased. These men who explored nature with techniques peculiar to their art had precisely the spirit and attitude of those other investigators of nature who founded modern science by means of their mathematics and experiments. In fact, during the Renaissance, art was regarded as a form of knowledge and a science. It aspired to the status of the four Platonic 'arts': arithmetic, geometry, harmony (music), and astronomy. Geometry was expected to supply the badge of respectability. Equally enticing as a goal in the development of a scientific system of perspective was the possibility of achieving unity of design.

The science of painting was founded by Brunelleschi, who worked out a system of perspective by 1425. He taught Donatello, Masaccio, Fra Filippo, and others. The first written account, the *della Pittura* of Leone Battista Alberti, was published in 1435. Alberti said in this treatise on painting that the first requirement of the painter is to know geometry. The arts are learned by reason and method; they are mastered by practice. In so far as painting is concerned, Alberti believed that nature could be improved on with the aid of mathematics, and towards this end he advocated the use of the mathematical system of perspective known as the focused system.

The great master of perspective and, incidentally, one of the best mathematicians of the fifteenth century was Piero della Francesca. His text *De Prospettiva Pingendi* added considerably to Alberti's material, though he took a slightly different approach. In this book Piero came close to identifying painting with perspective. During the last twenty years of his life he wrote three treatises to show how the visible world could be reduced to mathematical order by the principles of perspective and solid geometry.

The most famous of the artists who contributed to the science of perspective was Leonardo da Vinci. This striking figure of incredible physical strength and unparalleled mental endowment prepared for painting by deep and extensive studies in anatomy, perspective, geometry, physics, and chemistry. His attitude towards perspective was part and parcel of his philosophy of art. He opened his *Trattato della Pittura* with the words, 'Let no one who is not a mathematician read my works'. The object of painting, he insisted, is to reproduce nature and the merit of painting lies in the exactness of the reproduction. Even a purely imaginative creation must appear as if it could exist in nature. Painting, then, is a science and like all sciences must be based on mathematics, 'for no human inquiry can be called science unless it pursues its path through mathematical exposition and demonstration'. Again, 'The man who discredits the supreme certainty of mathematics is feeding on confusion, and can never silence the contradictions of sophistical sciences, which lead to eternal quackery'. Leonardo scorned those who thought they could ignore theory and produce art by mere practice: rather, 'Practice must always be founded on sound theory'. Perspective he described as the 'rudder and guide rope' of painting.

The most influential of the artists who wrote on perspective was Albrecht Dürer. Dürer learned the principles of perspective from the Italian masters and returned to Germany to continue his studies. His popular and widely read treatise *Underweysung der Messung mit dem Zyrkel und Rychtscheyd* (1528) affirmed that the perspective basis of a picture should not be drawn free-hand but constructed according to mathematical principles. Actually, the Renaissance painters were incomplete in their treatment of the principles of perspective. Mathematicians of a later period, notably Brook Taylor and J. H. Lambert, wrote definitive works.

It is fair to state that almost all the great artists of the fifteenth and early sixteenth centuries sought to incorporate mathematical principles and mathematical harmonies in their paintings, with realistic perspective a specific and major goal. Signorelli, Bramante, Michelangelo, and Raphael, among others, were deeply interested in mathematics and in its application to art. They deliberately executed difficult postures, developed and handled foreshortening with amazing facility, and at times even suppressed passion and feeling, all in order to display the scientific elements in their work. These masters were aware that art, with all its use of individual imagination, is subject to laws.

The basic principle of the mathematical system which these artists developed may be explained in terms used by Alberti, Leonardo, and Dürer. These men imagined that the artist's canvas is a glass screen through which he looks at the scene to be painted, just as we might look through a window to a scene outside. From one eye, which is held fixed, lines of light are imagined to go to each point of the scene. This set of lines is called a *projection*. Where each of these lines pierces the glass screen a point is marked on the screen. This set of points, called a *section*, creates the same impression on the eye as does the scene itself. These artists then decided that realistic painting must produce on canvas the location, size, and relative positions of objects exactly as they would appear on a glass screen interposed between the eye and the scene. In fact, Alberti proclaimed that the picture is a section of the projection.…

Before we examine some great paintings designed according to the system of focused perspective we should point out that the system does not furnish a faithful reproduction of what the eye sees. The principle that a painting must be a section of a projection requires, as already stated, that horizontal parallel lines which are parallel to the plane of the canvas, as well as vertical parallel lines, are to be drawn parallel. But the eye viewing such lines finds that they appear to meet just as other sets of parallel lines do. Hence in this respect at least the focused system is not visually correct. A more fundamental criticism is the fact that the eye does not see straight lines at all. The reader may convince himself of this fact if he will imagine himself in an aeroplane looking down on two perfectly parallel, horizontal railroad tracks. In each direction the tracks appear to meet on the horizon. Two straight lines, however, can meet in only one point. Obviously, then, since the tracks meet at the two horizon points, to the eye they must be curves. The Greeks and Romans had recognized that straight lines appear curved to the eye. Indeed, Euclid said so in his *Optics*. But the focused system ignores this fact of perception. Neither does the system take into account the fact that we actually see with two eyes, each of which receives a slightly different impression. Moreover, these eyes are not rigid but move as the spectator surveys a scene. Finally, the focused system ignores the fact that the retina of the eye on which the light rays impinge is a curved surface, not a photographic plate, and that seeing is as much a reaction of the brain as it is a purely physiological process.

In view of these deficiencies in the system, why did the artists adopt it? It was, of course, a considerable improvement over the inadequate systems known to the fourteenth century. More important to the fifteenth- and sixteenth-century artists was the fact that the system was a thoroughly mathematical one. To people already impressed with the importance of mathematics in understanding nature, the attainment of a satisfactory mathematical system of perspective pleased them so much that they were blind to all its deficiencies. In fact, the artists believed it to be as true as Euclidean geometry itself.

Let us now examine the progeny of the wedding of geometry and painting. One of the first painters to apply the science of perspective initiated by Brunelleschi was Masaccio (1401–28). Although later paintings will show more clearly the influence of the new science, Masaccio's 'The Tribute Money' is far more realistic than anything done earlier. Vasari said that Masaccio was the first artist to attain the imitation of things as they really are. This particular painting shows great depth, spaciousness, and naturalism. The individual figures are massive; they exist in space and their bodies are more real than Giotto's. The figures stand on their own feet. Masaccio was also the first to use a technique which supplements geometry, namely, aerial perspective. By diminishing the intensity of the colour as well as the size of objects farther in the background, distance is suggested. Masaccio was, in fact, a master at handling light and shade.

One of the major contributors to the science of perspective was Uccello (1397–1475). His interest in the subject was so intense that Vasari said Uccello 'would remain the long night in his study to work out the vanishing points of his perspective' and when summoned to bed by his wife replied, 'How sweet a thing is this perspective'. He took pleasure in investigating difficult problems, and he was so distracted by his passion for exact perspective that he failed to apply his full powers to painting. Painting was an occasion for solving problems and displaying his mastery of perspective. Actually his success was not complete. His figures are generally crowded on one another and his mastery of depth was imperfect.

Unfortunately, the best examples of Uccello's perspective have been so much damaged by time that they cannot be reproduced. One scene from the sequence entitled 'Desecration of the Host' does give some indication of his work. His 'Perspective Study of a Chalice' shows the complexity of surfaces, lines, and curves involved in an accurate perspective drawing.

The artist who perfected the science of perspective was Piero della Francesca (1416–92). This highly intellectual painter had a passion for geometry, and planned all his works mathematically to the last detail. The placement of each figure was calculated so as to be correct in relation to other figures and to the organization of the painting as a whole. He even used geometrical forms for parts of the body and objects of dress and he loved smooth curved surfaces and solidity.

Piero's 'The Flagellation' is a masterpiece of perspective. The choice of principal vanishing point and the accurate use of the principles of the focused system tie the characters in the rear of the courtyard to those in front, while the objects are all accommodated to the clearly delimited space. The diminution of the black inlays on the marble floor is also precisely calculated. A drawing in Piero's book on perspective shows the immense labour which went into this painting. Here as well as in other paintings Piero used aerial perspective to enhance the impression of depth. The whole painting is so carefully planned that movement is sacrificed to unity of design.

Piero's 'Resurrection' is judged by some critics to be one of the supreme works of painting in the entire world. It is almost architectural in design. The perspective is unusual: there are two points of vision and therefore two principal vanishing points. As is evident from the fact that we see the necks of two of the sleeping soldiers from below, one principal vanishing point is in the middle of the sarcophagus. Then unconsciously the eye is carried up to the second principal vanishing point which is in the face of Christ. The two pictures, that is the lower and upper parts, are separated by a natural boundary, the upper edge of the sarcophagus, so that the change in point of view is not disturbing. By making the hills rise rather sharply Piero unified the two parts at the same time that he supplied a natural-appearing background for the upper one. It has sometimes been said that Piero's intense love for perspective made his pictures too mathematical and therefore cool and impersonal. However, a look at the sad, haunting, and forgiving countenance of Christ shows that Piero was capable of expressing delicate shades of emotion.

Leonardo da Vinci (1452-1519) produced many excellent examples of perfect perspective. This truly scientific mind and subtle aesthetic genius made numerous detailed studies for each painting. His best-known work and perhaps the most famous of all paintings is an excellent example of perfect perspective. The 'Last Supper' is designed to give exactly the impression that would be made on the eye in real life. The viewer feels that he is in the room. The receding lines on the walls, floor, and ceiling not only convey depth clearly but converge to one point deliberately chosen to be in the head of Christ so that attention focuses on Him. It should be noticed incidentally, that the twelve apostles are arranged in four groups of three each and are symmetrically disposed on each side of Christ. The figure of Christ Himself forms an equilateral triangle; this element of the design was intended to express the balance of sense, reason, and body. Leonardo's painting should be compared with Duccio's 'The Last Supper'.

A few more examples of paintings that incorporate excellent perspective will indicate perhaps the widespread appeal and application of the new science. Though Botticelli (1444-1510) is most widely known for such paintings as 'Spring' and the 'Birth of Venus' where the artist expresses himself in pattern, lines, and curves and where realism is not an objective, he was capable of excellent perspective. One of the finest of his numerous works, 'The Calumny of Apelles', shows his mastery of the science. Each object is sharply drawn. The various parts of the throne and of the buildings are well executed and the foreshortening of all the objects is correct.

A painter who exhibited great skill in perspective was Mantegna (1431–1506). Anatomy and perspective were ideals with him. He chose difficult problems and used perspective to achieve harsh realism and boldness. In his 'St James Led to Execution' he deliberately chose an eccentric point of view. The principal vanishing point is just below the bottom of the painting and to the right of centre. The whole scene is successfully treated from this unusual point of view.

The sixteenth century witnessed the culmination of the great Renaissance developments in realistic painting. The masters displayed perfect perspective and form, and emphasized space and colour. The ideal of form was loved so much that artists were indifferent to content. The distinguished pupil of Leonardo and Michelangelo, Raphael (1483–1520), supplied many excellent examples of the ideals, standards, and accomplishments towards which the preceding centuries had been striving. His 'School of Athens' portrays a dignified architectural setting in which harmonious arrangement, mastery of perspective, and exactness of proportions are clear. This painting is of interest not merely because of its superb treatment of space and depth, but because it evidences the veneration that the Renaissance intellectuals had for the Greek masters. Plato and Aristotle, left and right, are the central figures. At Plato's left is Socrates. In the left foreground Pythagoras writes in a book. In the right foreground Euclid or Archimedes stoops to demonstrate some theorem. To the right of this figure Ptolemy holds a sphere. Musicians, arithmeticians, and grammarians complete the assemblage.

The Venetian masters of the sixteenth century subordinated line to colour and light and shade. Nevertheless they too were masters of perspective. The expression of space is fully three-dimensional, and organization and perspective are clearly felt. Tintoretto (1518–94) is representative of this school. His 'Transfer of the Body of St Mark' shows perfect treatment of depth; the foreshortening of the figures in the foreground should be noticed.

We shall take time for just one more example. We have already mentioned Dürer (1472–1528) as one of the writers on the subject of perspective who greatly influenced painters north of the Alps. His

'St Jerome in his Study', an engraving on copper, shows what Dürer himself could do in practice. The principal vanishing point is at the right centre of the picture. The effect of the design is to make the spectator feel that he is in the room just a few feet away from St Jerome.

The examples given above of paintings which use the focused system of perspective could be multiplied a thousandfold. These few are sufficient, however, to illustrate how the use of mathematical perspective emancipated figures from the gold background of medieval painting and set them free to roam the streets and hills of the natural world. The examples also illustrate a secondary value in the use of focused perspective, namely, that of promoting the unity of composition of the painting. Our account of the rise of this system may have shown, too, how the theorems of mathematics proper and a philosophy of nature in which mathematics was dominant determined the course of Western painting. Though modern painting has departed sharply from a veridical description of nature, the focused system is still taught in the art schools and is applied wherever it seems important to achieve a realistic effect.

Mathematics in Western Culture
pp. 126–46
Allen and Unwin 1954

II

The Role of Experiment

The seventeenth century was above all an age in which the idea of experimenting came into its own. Experiment, rather than reliance upon authority, was seen as the main route to the advancement of learning and Newton's Optics may stand as a classical example of it. How did this belief in experimental method arise? Many argue that it was connected in some way with puritanism and with economic advance, taken in conjunction with Bacon's ideas. Lynn Thorndike, on the other hand is much more sceptical. It is an essential part of his argument that men like Bacon, for all their experimental zeal, could be as uncritical as any medieval thinker. Indeed experiments might well be carried out to confirm the opinion of a recognized authority rather than to undermine it. In the second extract printed here Thorndike maintains that the Royal Society, which was Baconian in inspiration, was far from scientific in the modern sense. A more favourable view of Bacon and of the Royal Society is to be found below in Zilsel (p. 96) and Johnson (p. 50).

3 Francis Bacon – A Critical View

L. THORNDIKE

If parts allure thee, think how Bacon shined,
The wisest, brightest, meanest of mankind!

ALEXANDER POPE

Without wholeheartedly subscribing to this violent antithesis, it may be said that, as Bacon was impeached as Lord Chancellor for accepting gifts of money from suitors while their cases were still pending, so there has recently been a tendency among historians of science to censure him, as a professed natural philosopher and reformer of learning, for taking what did not belong to him in that sphere also, and failing to own his debt to predecessors such as Roger Bacon in the thirteenth century. This note of censure has replaced a former chorus of adulation

31

based upon ignorance and misapprehension of the Middle Ages and typified by the following quotation:

'It took more than twelve centuries for a Bacon to rescue the principle of scientific causality from a world which had become enveloped in medievalism.'

However, even an early Victorian like Whewell wrote over a century ago that Francis Bacon's precepts as to scientific method 'are now practically useless'. And back in 1861 Draper, after condemning Bacon for rejecting the Copernican system, and after stating that 'his chief admirers have been persons of a literary turn', that he never accomplished any great practical discovery and that 'few scientific pretenders have made more mistakes' than he, concluded:

It is time that the sacred name of philosophy should be severed from its long connexion with that of one who was a pretender in science, a time-serving politician, an insidious lawyer, a corrupt judge, a treacherous friend, a bad man.'

We should perhaps remind ourselves that the *Advancement of Learning* appeared in English in 1605, and *Novam Organum* in Latin in 1620, the year before Bacon's impeachment and retirement from public life. Other scientific or pseudo-scientific treatises were published during his last years or posthumously, as was the case with *Sylva sylvarum*, a collection of a thousand observations and experiments arranged in ten centuries, in 1627; *Descriptio globi intellectualis* and other treatises, in 1652; *Historia Densi et rari*, in 1658: yet others only in 1679, 1688 and 1734.

Francis Bacon resembled his thirteenth-century namesake Roger not only in some of his leading ideas but in his plan and method of composition. As Roger planned a comprehensive work of philosophy which he never completed, but of which some of his extant writings were probably intended to serve as sections, so Francis planned an *Instauratio Magna*, and his philosophical works consist in large parts of 'works published, or designed for publication as parts of the *Instauratio Magna*'. And as Roger left various versions as treatises, so another chief group of Francis's works were 'originally designed for parts of the *Instauratio Magna*', but superseded or abandoned, and are further described by their editors as writings which Bacon himself would not have cared to preserve and which contain:

'but little matter of which the substance may not be found in one part or another of the preceding volumes, reduced to the shape in which he thought it would be most effective.'

In the dedication to King James I of the Great Instauration, Bacon represented his position as completely novel, saying, 'It is as least new, even in its very nature', and that the

'only wonderful circumstance is that the first conception of the matter and so deep suspicions of prevalent notions should ever have entered into any person's mind'.

By making a virtue of not citing authorities he avoided any mention of the sources of his ideas. This was bad enough, but he made it worse by assailing some of the greatest names in the past. Thus, after having spoken depreciatingly of Aristotle, Plato and Ramus, he continued:

'Let us now proceed to physicians. I see Galen, a man of the narrowest mind, a forsaker of experience, and a most vain pretender.'

No statement could be more unjust and erroneous. Of all extant ancient writers Galen approaches most closely to the conception of experimental method, and was often cited by medieval authors for the recognition of experience as a criterion of truth. There is a trifle more of verisimilitude in Bacon's scornful characterization of Hippocrates as one who:

'sheltered by brevity . . . does nothing but either deliver certain sophistications in sentences abrupt and suspended, thus withdrawing them from confutation; or invest with stateliness the observations of rustics'.

But when we come to consider Bacon's own medicine, I feel sure that the reader will prefer that of Galen and Hippocrates. And when Bacon exhorts us to attend to things themselves, he is only repeating what Galen – and many others – had said long ago.

Bacon's defects in the role of the protagonist of experimental science did not escape the eyes of his contemporaries. Mersenne in 1625 made three criticisms of him: first, that he should have consulted the savants of different countries before laying down rules which were either practised already or of no use; second, that he often proposed experiments which had already been performed; third, that he introduced innovations in terminology which would retard scientific progress.

Yet the title of Lord Verulam under which his works appeared commanded universal respect in England and abroad. He possessed undoubted ability, breadth of view and intellectual insight. He was not a scientist by profession or training: few men as yet were. But in a sense there was something to be said for having an outsider and a man of good general education – rather than an astronomer or astrologer or chymist or alchemist or physician or pharmacist or mathematician or mechanic – to consider the general problem of natural and experimental science. Bacon was not bound by any university curriculum or professional limits. His wide and restless curiosity kept him out of ruts and beaten paths, though it did not keep him from trespassing on others' preserves as if he had an intellectual right of way or of eminent domain. He marked, in the British Isles at least, that amateurish interest of the upper classes in natural science and experimentation which led to the founding of the Royal Society. As an outsider he naturally joined to the credulity of the layman a certain amount of lay contemptuous scepticism for the niceties and the traditions of academic and professional science. He also tended to conjectural speculation on the one hand, and occasionally to express himself in Elizabethan terms of metaphorical fancy rather than of literal science.

Bacon called for 'an absolute regeneration of science', a fresh start – as Descartes was to do again presently, 'an entirely different way from any known to our predecessors'. For one thing, he wished to keep natural philosophy unadulterated, and to mark off natural science as a distinct field and discipline. He complained that Aristotle had mixed it with logic; Plato with natural theology; and the Neo-Platonists with mathematics. This suggests what from the standpoint of modern science was his chief defect, his total disregard of mathematical method. He spoke of pure mathematics, as, like the game of tennis, of no use in itself but as good exercise to cure intellectual defects. He further held that attention to final causes and the argument from design belong to metaphysics, but serve only to obstruct the search for immediate physical causes. He was therefore critical of such statements as that the clouds are to water the earth, the leaves to protect the fruit, the bones to support the frame, the skins of animals to protect them from heat or cold, and the eyelids to protect the sight. But such criticism perhaps accords none too well with the doctrine of evolution and survival of the fittest.

Bacon would study nature as a whole and all at once. He wants a broad collection of particular facts 'capable of informing the mind', something on the order, it would seem, of a revision and reformation of Pliny's Natural History. He speaks slightingly of the experimental specialization of Gilbert with the magnet, and of that of the alchemists. Bacon's attitude was the not uncommon one of condemnation of alchemists for their endless efforts, perpetual hope deferred, and waste of time and money, along with admission that they had made not a few discoveries and useful inventions. And, of course, he had his own little recipes for making gold.

Like Aldrovandi, Bacon would try to exclude fables and marvels, curiosities and traditions. He would furthermore not merely collect observations and experiences like ants or the Empirics – as a matter of fact, that was often as far as he got – but would work them over by the indictive method as bees make honey, and ascend from facts and experiments to laws of nature. Mere observation, as in Aristotle's History of Animals, is not enough; purposive artificial experimentation is further required. Bacon realized the need of apparatus and expenditure – as indeed did Gilbert and the chemists – and urged original research and endowment thereof, new inventions and things out of the common track. I must confess that I fail to appreciate his criticizing the naturalists of his time for observing the differences between various animals, plants and minerals instead of noting their resemblances. If differences are noted, the residue will be resemblances and vice versa. What is the difference? Or, one might argue, if you note the differences, you are assuming or approaching some norm from which they differ; while, if you note resemblances and analogies, you appear to be picking these out of a chaotic sea of differences. One might argue either way. . . .

In conclusion there is not much more that one can say for Francis Bacon. He was a crooked chancellor in a moral sense and a crooked naturalist in an intellectual and scientific sense. He did not think straight. Or put it in this way, if you prefer. Even a Lord High Chancellor, even a Francis Bacon, could not think straight when he thought as a naturalist and tried to amass 'experiments' on the one hand and grapple with magical tradition and superstition on the other hand. The path of magic and experimental science was no straight and narrow one; it was not true, and its course did not run smooth. It was a relatively easy thing to criticize the past and present state of learning, and to advocate a new programme, including 'experimental science'. Roger Bacon had done it three and a half centuries before. But when it came to getting down off one's high horse of generalities and putting one's shoulder to the problem of particular phenomena of nature and dealing with specific facts and beliefs and traditions and errors, Francis Bacon was as helpless as Pliny had been in antiquity or as anyone else was in the early seventeenth century. The best that one can say for him is that he really tried.

It must be admitted, however, that he was much cited and admired by many writers of his century, Mersenne being something of an exception. And his tendency to explain natural phenomena by the action of corporeal spirits became widespread and general.

History of Magic and Experimental Science
vol. vii, pp. 63–88
Columbia University Press 1958

4 Were the Scientific Academies Unscientific?

L. THORNDIKE

It has also been said that the *Proceedings of the Royal Society* in Boyle's time abounded in 'papers on the medicinal power of gems and the astrological influences of the planets as physical problems worthy of the new experimental methods of inquiry. Similarly it has been recognized that many of the members of the Royal Society in the seventeenth century 'were merely dilettantes seeking amusement', and that the early records of the Society are a 'weird agglomeration of trivialities and discoveries which the attrition of subsequent investigation has shown to be of basic importance'.

In the first volume of the *Philosophical Transactions* of the Royal Society in 1665 are communications from Boyle concerning a 'very odd monstrous calf' and the monstrous head of a colt. Also some 'observations and experiments upon May-Dew', which would putrefy in the shade but not in the sun, and the killing of a rattlesnake in Virginia in July, 1657, in less than half an hour by holding bruised pennyroyal or dittany to its nose, and the additional observation that no rattlesnakes are seen where this herb grows. Secrets are mentioned every now and then, such as an admirable secret, not yet revealed, to keep ships from being worm-eaten. The Portuguese build their ships of hard wood and scorch them, while a Londoner suggests the use of pitch. A letter from Steno reports that a knight named Corvini assured him of the following experiment with a salamander which he had imported from the Indies. When Corvini threw it into the fire, it soon swelled up and vomited a quantity of thick slimy matter which quenched the neighbouring coals. As soon as they rekindled, the salamander put them out again in the same way, and by this means saved itself for two hours. It lived for nine months afterwards, although for eleven months it had no other sustenance that what it got by licking the earth on which it was brought from the Indies, and which it moistened with its urine, as the earth dried up. When Corvini substituted Italian soil, the salamander expired in three days' time. New teeth crop out in a man of eighty-one and a woman of seventy-five.

Monstrosities continued to be recorded in subsequent volumes. A monstrous birth was in the form of an ape with a mass of flesh over its shoulders like a little cloak, because the mother had seen an ape thus clothed upon the stage, when she had gone five months with child. Passing over two monstrous sheep, we note a headless child which lived for four days, thus refuting the theory of Descartes that the pineal gland is the connection between mind and body. Or we hear of hailstones eight, nine and twelve inches in circumference and ninety-six stones in a boy. Somewhat fantastic experiments also continue, such as Hooke's preserving animals alive by blowing air with bellows through their lungs, or Dr Richard Lower's making a dog draw its breath 'exactly like a wind-broken horse'. Yet along with such trivialities are announced Mariotte's discovery of the blind spot by experiment, and Pecquet's showing, also by experiment, that it is in the retina, not in the optic nerve.

How British scientists reacted to the publication of the German physicians may be further illustrated by a review that appeared in *Philosophical Transactions* of the volume for the years 1673 and 1674 of *Ephemerides medico-physicae Germanicae*. The reviewer states that it contains 210 observations, 'among which not a few seem considerable and uncommon'. For example: *menses* coming at eight and nine years of age; a prince that lived a long time despite great and dangerous diseases; a preservation from drunkenness by the gaping of a suture of the head; a case of scurvy cured by a dog's licking the parts affected, and then the cure of the dog, which had become 'altogether scabby', by use of *Mercurius dulcis*; two men troubled with haemorrhoids from youth to the ages of eighty and ninety respectively; stone in the bladder cured by use of an oil from black flints 'such as we strike fire with'; fomentations made with a decoction of ants 'very anti-paralytical'; a girl of eight who greedily devoured 'a great store' of mortar without other apparent ill effect than paleness; a man at Prague who ate a whole live hog piecemeal with the bristles on; and a Bavarian prince who not only was able to lift a weight of 340 pounds but also to 'throw it a considerable distance'. Before such science, magic might well hang its head and take a back seat.

As for topics considered by the members of the English Royal Society, its contemporary historian, Sprat, lists along with such practical or would-be practical matters as growing potatoes, planting of hops, and making wine from sugar-canes, and along with scientific subjects such as the manner of the circulation of the blood in fish, strata seen at a well at Amsterdam and in diverse cliffs, a report of two new stars observed in 1666, one in Andromeda, the other in Cygnus, and both in the same place where they appeared sixty years before and had not been since, the following more curious and marvellous topics. A way of turning water into earth, a reported rain of fish and frogs, that silkworms in Virginia are not hurt by thunder, of swallows living after they had been frozen underwater, of barnacles and solon geese, of several monsters, and of sympathetic cures and trials. For, as Sprat remarks later, 'there are many qualities and figures and powers of things that break the common laws and transgress the standing rules of nature.' Even in the early eighteenth century Woodward was expelled from the Council of the Royal Society for refusing to apologize for remarks he had made reflecting upon Dr Hans Sloane who had stated that gall-stones caused colic, which Woodward denied.

On March 27, 1686, Halley, as secretary of the Royal Society wrote to Ashe of the Philosophical Society at Dublin:

> 'Your new method of demonstrating the knottiest Propositions of Euclid, your new-invented Dial, your Experiments of Injections of Liquors into Animals, and the account of your mathematical Girl, are things that will be very acceptable to us: as likewise whatsoever, whether Natural, Artificial or Mathematical Curiosity comes before you.'

On May 27 of the same year he acknowledges the receipt from Molyneux of the same Irish society of:

> 'the figure of the Horny Girle, which is certainly a most extraordinary curiosity, and which I belive very much puzles the Physicians to account for; wee are made to belive we shall see her here at Bartholomew faire'.

On July 9 he writes to yet another correspondent:

> 'I have this day seen a great curiosity viz a Calicoe shirt brought from India, which is wove without a seam all of one piece, which I should have thought impossible had I not seen it. It explains the Scripture relations of our Saviours coat which was without seam.'

On November 13 he writes to the noted mathematician Wallis:

> 'The child you mention to have seen with 6 fingers on a hand and as many toes on each foot is a great curiosity, especially if they be so contrived that the hand be not therby made less fit to do its office. Nor is the quantity of water found in the Dropsicall maid less prodigious, it being hardly conceavable how the Muscles of the Abdomen should be distended to so great a Capacity.'

A little later in the same letter he mentions a dwarf only sixteen inches high 'said to have been presented lately to the French King'. The next year in another letter to Wallis he tells somewhat sceptically of a 'very odd relation of an Hermaphrodite' at Toulouse. In 1696 Halley writes to Hans Sloane concerning a monstrous birth from a greyhound of which Wallis had informed the Society.

History of Magic and Experimental Science
vol. viii, pp. 252–6
Columbia University Press 1958

III

The Mathematical Revolution

What requires explanation is the enthusiasm for mathematics which seized so many able men in the sixteenth and seventeenth centuries. Several possible reasons have been put forward. Alexander Koyré, for example, is not alone in attributing this to the revival of Platonic philosophy which took place during the Renaissance. Others, among them Professor Clagett, regard the mathematical achievement of the seventeenth century as developing naturally out of the middle ages. Another view finds the cause of mathematical progress in the stimulus which was given by essentially practical naval problems, raised in the course of exploration. F. R. Johnson may stand as an example of this point of view, which is also to be found in the work of Christopher Hill and Edgar Zilsel. An interpretation in which the dockyard looms larger than the university in the rise of science is one which many Marxists find attractive.

5 Medieval Mechanics

M. CLAGETT

The key role of physics in general and mechanics in particular in the development of modern science has often been recognized, for it was in the mechanical area of early modern physics that the first thorough-going application was made of the mathematical and experimental techniques so crucial to the growth of modern science. But an admission of the important role of mechanics in the early modern period does not mean that we must search only the mature mechanical works of the seventeenth century for the beginnings of modern science. It is an obvious fact to the historian of science that the physical concepts of

Galileo or a Descartes, or even a Newton, radical as they may seem, were conditioned in many ways by the ancient and medieval learning that survived into the early modern period. And thus anyone who is honestly interested in the enormously complex *historical* process of the formation of modern science must examine in detail the germinal concepts of the preceding periods. Such an examination will reveal the elements of continuity (and thereby also of novelty) in the new science. This examination will give some insight into how a protoscientific theory was criticized and emended until it was no longer a cogent whole. It will also show how the very points of criticism of the older system became points of departure for the new. It will show, in short, how medieval mechanics – largely Aristotelian with some traces of Archimedean character – was continually modified to the point where it was seriously undermined, thus requiring a new mechanical system – and it was the Galilean–Newtonian system of the seventeenth century that fulfilled that requirement. . . .

Medieval mechanics as a field of careful historical research is certainly not one with a long history. The delay in research in medieval mechanics was, I believe, due to the common view held in some quarters since the seventeenth century that science – and particularly mechanics – was an invention of the seventeenth century, and, if it had any significant antecedents, those antecedents lay not in the Middle Ages but rather in antiquity. And since there is an element of truth in this view, even those early students who gave some attention to medieval mechanics, such as Charles Thurot and Giovanni Vailati in the nineteenth century, treated medieval opinion merely as an offshoot of Greek mechanics and not as an object of independent research. Thurot's investigations of 1868–9 into the history of the principle of Archimedes, while they treated the medieval views of hydrostatics only incidentally, nevertheless had the distinct advantage of being based on the direct study of both manuscripts and early printed editions of the works of medieval authors. Vailati's important studies in the history of statics, originally published at the end of the nineteenth century (and later collected in his *Scritti* in 1911), concentrated on the antique period but were the first to recognize the importance of the statical texts attributed to the thirteenth-century mathematician Jordanus de Nemore in the growth of the concept of virtual velocities. However, unlike Thurot, Vailati did not investigate medieval manuscript sources.

Thus it was actually reserved to one individual to change the investigation of medieval mechanics from an incidental by path to a field of investigation where the principal objective of research was to estimate the view of the medieval schoolmen on mechanical problems. This was the eminent French scientist Pierre Duhem, whose *Les Origines de la statique*, (1905–6) brought to light the rich content of medieval statistical treatises that had received little or no attention prior to his time. His *Études sur Léonard de Vinci* (1906–13), although very badly organized, attempted the same thing for kinematics and dynamics. It was in the latter work that Duhem discussed the fruitful medieval emendations of the Aristotelian mechanics of free fall and projectile motion and first outlined the kinematic description of uniform and accelerated motion that took place at Oxford and Paris in the fourteenth century. It was as the result of Duhem's investigation of manuscripts and early printed sources that John Buridan, Nicole Oresme, and other schoolmen of fourteenth-century Paris and Oxford emerged as key figures in the development of late medieval physics. It was Duhem who uncovered the medieval *impetus* theory – a kind of protomomentum concept – which under the stimulation of the scholastic discussion of Buridan and others was to exert some influence on late medieval and even early modern physical thought. So rich were Duhem's investigations – partially emended and corrected by numerous articles in his monumental *Le Système du monde* (1913–16, 1954–57) – that one can say that in a sense the succeeding study of medieval mechanics has been largely devoted to an extension or refutation of Duhem's work.

But in spite of their obvious importance, Duhem's investigations were not without serious defects. He made extravagant claims for the modernity of medieval concepts. Thus Buridan's impetus theory appears to emerge in Duhem's hands as a theory of inertia; and Oresme is considered as the inventor of analytic geometry because of his system of graphing qualities and movements, and as a precursor of Copernicus because of his discussion of the possibility of the earth's rotation. Furthermore, Duhem's procedure of presenting only parts of crucial passages – often out of context and then only in French translation without the equivalent Latin passages – made it almost impossible to evaluate Duhem's judgements without an extensive search of the manuscripts. . . .

. . . It was only with the publication of Anneliese Maier's studies that Duhem's works were given a thoroughgoing review and revaluation. Her general conclusions are found in one of the most important of her many publications, *Die Vorlaufer Galileis im. 14. Jahrhundert* (1949). Miss Maier's work has been based on detailed manuscript investigations. The result of Maier's magnificent studies has been to place the mechanical ideas uncovered by Duhem in their proper medieval setting and to show their essential divergences from the later concepts of modern mechanics. Thus, to give only one example, Miss Maier shows that Buridan's *impetus* is at best to be considered a rejected analogue to momentum rather than identical to it. Furthermore, Miss Maier's studies opened up areas of medieval natural philosophy not studied by Duhem. . . . A less detailed but important critique of Duhem's thesis has been made by that eminent historian of mechanics, A. Koyré. His *Études Galiléennes* (1939) emphasizes the point that it was only when Galileo abandoned some of the medieval views (like one version of the impetus theory) that he made essential progress.

It should be obvious from a study of Duhem and his critics that the one essential for an adequate review of medieval mechanical doctrines is the publication of the texts on which judgements have to be made. Maier has already done important service by complementing her critical comments with the texts of important passages. Similarly the distinguished student of medieval philosophy, Ernest Moody, has demonstrated the importance of making available the full texts of some of the crucial scholastic treatises in which are found the most interesting of the medieval mechanical ideas. He first gave us the *Quaestiones super libris quattuor de caelo* of John Buridan in 1942, where are found in their full context many of Buridan's important ideas, including a discussion of the impetus theory, of the possible rotation of the earth, and so on. Moody also initiated the project, in which I joined him as collaborator, to make available *all* of the principal medieval statical treatises. This project resulted in a volume entitled the *Medieval Science of Weights* (1952), the first volume in the University of Wisconsin's *Publications in Medieval Science*. Our purpose in that volume was to present the complete texts so that historian and scientist alike could judge the claims of Duhem for the importance of medieval statics. . . .

One of the most precious heritages from Greece was the employment of mathematical-deductive proofs in statics. The form of such proofs originated about the time of Euclid and Archimedes and was stamped on most succeeding treatments of statics. In addition to inheriting the Greek form of proof and analysis, the medieval statical authors inherited several important theorems that were to become the focal points of both medieval and modern statics. Among these theorems we can single out the general law of the lever as applied to both straight and bent levers. Furthermore, the problem of the inclined plane, which leads to a correct procedure of analysing or resolving forces when properly solved (which it was not in antiquity), came into the Middle Ages and there received a brilliant and correct solution which in some respects surpasses both the solutions of Stevin and Galileo. Also inherited in primitive form was the principle of virtual velocities which is found in nascent form in the *Mechanica* attributed to Aristotle and more clearly in the *Mechanics* of Hero. We see that in the Middle Ages this principle was applied in the formal mathematical proofs of theorems relative to the law of the lever for straight and bent levers and to the equilibrium of weights on oppositely inclined planes. In essence all the medieval proofs show that unless the well-known lever and inclined plane theorems are accepted as true, the principle of virtual velocities is violated. In such proofs the medieval students were clearly foreshadowing the modern dynamic approach to statics that only became thoroughly established with the work of John Bernoulli and Lagrange, although Stevin, Galileo, and other scientists of the early modern period were not uninfluenced by this approach. It was probably in the works attributed to the famous thirteenth-century mathematician Jordanus de Nemore that a new and important form of the principle of virtual velocities originated. The study of the subsequent history of medieval statics after the first half of the thirteenth century shows that, while further original contributions do not appear to have been made, there was at least some continuing treatment of statics and some improvement in the precise statement of the principles.

The Science of Mechanics in the Middle Ages
pp. xvii–xxiv
University of Wisconsin Press 1959

6 Mathematics and the Practical World

F. R. JOHNSON

... In his will, [1575] Sir Thomas Gresham had provided that the professors of his foundation should be unmarried, should occupy his mansion house and have free use of its gardens and all other appurtenances, and that each professor should receive an annual stipend of fifty pounds, a handsome salary in those days. The Mercers' Company was charged with the original selection and the payment of the professors of law, physic, and rhetoric, and the Mayor and Aldermen of the City of London with the selection and payment of the professors of divinity, music, geometry and astronomy.

Soon after the death of Lady Gresham [1596] brought this benefaction under their control, the City of London and the Mercers' Company sent out letters to Oxford and Cambridge Universities asking for the recommendation of suitable candidates for the posts that had been placed in their charge.

In the final choice of the seven original professors, the two universities were equally represented (John Bull, the first music professor, was a graduate of both). The first professor of astronomy was Edward Brerewood, an Oxford man. The first geometry professor was Henry Briggs, a graduate of St John's College, Cambridge, and one of the ablest mathematicians of the day. His contribution to the development of logarithms is familiar to all, for it was he who saw the great practical advantage of using the number ten as a base, and devoted his energies to computing the Briggsian tables of logarithms, and to popularizing the use of logarithms throughout the scientific world.

To Briggs, more than to anyone else, was due the immediate establishment of Gresham College as a meeting-place of scientists and a clearing-house for scientific information. The comfortable and spacious quarters of the Gresham professors, the central location of the college in London, and the eminence of Briggs himself all contributed towards this end. Briggs was the friend and the collaborator of most of the noted scientists of his day. Thomas Blundeville, Sir Thomas Chaloner, William Barlowe, Marke Ridley, Edward Wright, and William Gilbert were among the leading English scientists with whom Briggs was associated. The relations of this group may be traced in the scientific publications of the day, and in other contemporary records.

Gilbert acknowledges help from Barlowe in the research on magnetism that was set forth in his De Magnete. Edward Wright, whose great work was the reform of the theory of navigation and the correction of Mercator's projection, contributed an important preface to Gilbert's work. Blundeville, in a work of his own, published in 1602, included an appendix by Gilbert, describing two magnets he had invented, and Briggs, to this appendix, contributed a table which he had calculated for the use of these magnets. Both Wright and Briggs co-operated in making Napier's invention of logarithms known to English mathematicians. Wright translated Napier's book on logarithms into English immediately, and Briggs added a special preface to the work, together with a short treatise of his own on the methods of interpolation when using the tables. In this preface, Briggs mentions his teaching 'the meaning and the use of this booke at Gresham house'.

Another noted member of this group was William Bedwell, one of the most learned men of his day, the father of Arabic studies in England, and one of the Westminster Company of translators who prepared the King James version of the Bible. Bedwell was also a mathematical scholar, and published a number of mathematical works and translations, chief among these being a translation of Peter Ramus's geometry, greatly enlarged by Bedwell himself. In 1601 Bedwell became rector of St Ethelburga's in Bishopsgate Street, close by Gresham College. Thus a friendship with Briggs born of common interests, which probably had begun at Cambridge – for the two were contemporaries there – was cemented and continued throughout both their lives. In 1606 Briggs sent to Mr Clerke of Gravesend a description of a special type of ruler invented by Bedwell. His correspondence was probably with the John Clerke who, in 1636, after the death of both Briggs and Bedwell, published his friend Bedwell's book, dedicating it to John Greaves, who had become professor of geometry at Gresham College in 1631, just a year before Bedwell's death. This preface indicated that Greaves's short but happy friendship with Bedwell dated from the time Greaves came from Oxford to London in 1630 to assume his duties at Gresham College. Bedwell, in his own preface, mentions his friendship with Briggs, and states that Briggs had examined the work and had repeatedly urged him to publish it.

Still another distinguished member of the Gresham College circle in Briggs's time, and later, was the famous mathematician William Oughtred, who made important contributions to mathematical notation and invented the rectilinear and circular slide rules. By his private teaching Oughtred greatly furthered the progress of mathematical knowledge in England, and he numbered among his pupils Seth Ward and John Wallis. Oughtred, from 1610 to his death in 1660, was rector of Albury, near Guildford in Surrey, and on each of his journeys to London visited his friends at Gresham College. In a pamphlet published in 1633, he describes a visit made in 1618:

> In the Spring 1618 I being at London went to see my honoured friend Master *Henry Briggs* at Gresham Colledge: who then brought me acquainted

with Master *Gunter* lately chosen Astronomie reader there, and was at that time in Doctour *Brooks* his chamber. With whom falling into speech about his quadrant, I shewed him my Horizontall Instrument: He viewed it very heedfully: and questioned about the projecture and use thereof, often saying these words, it is a very good one. And not long after he delivered to Master *Briggs* to be sent to me mine owne Instrument printed off from one cut in brasse: which afterwards I understood he presented to the right Honourable the Earle of Bridgewater, and in his booke of the Sector printed sixe yeares after, among other projections he setteth down this.

Oughtred is writing nearly fifteen years after his visit, and gives the erroneous impression that in 1618 Gunter was already Gresham Professor of Astronomy. It is worth noting, therefore, that Oughtred found Gunter, who was not elected professor until the following March, occupying rooms in Gresham College.

From the early years of the seventeenth century there is evidence of a close association, in scientific investigations, of the Gresham College professors and the sea captains, the shipbuilders, and the administrative officials of the English Navy. Briggs, in 1609, served with Sir Thomas Chaloner in judging a controversy between two factions among the shipwrights over some innovations in design which Phineas Pett had introduced. John Clerke, whom we have seen as the friend and correspondent of Bedwell and Briggs, is probably the John Clerke who, in 1628, is found sharing with one John Cowper the grant of the office of Surveyor and Keeper of His Majesty's Armoury in the Tower and at East Greenwich.

In 1619, just before Briggs left Gresham College to become the first Savilian Professor of Geometry at Oxford, Edmund Gunter was chosen Gresham Professor of Astronomy. Gunter must have begun, at Briggs's instigation, the work of calculating the logarithms of the trigonometric functions even before his election, for his *Canon Triangulorum* was published early in 1620. After Briggs's departure for Oxford, Gunter became the central figure of the Gresham College scientific circle, and continued so until his death in December 1626. With Gunter, the association of Gresham College and its circle with a group of navy officials stationed at the naval base across the Thames at Deptford continued.

The key figure uniting the two groups was an able mathematician and scientist, John Wells, who, from 1606 until his death late in the year 1635, held the important office of Keeper of His Majesty's Naval Stores at Deptford. He was a friend and fellow-worker successively of

Briggs, Gunter, and, finally, Henry Gellibrand, who, in 1626, succeeded Gunter as professor of astronomy at Gresham College. . . .

As Keeper of His Majesties Stores at the Navy Yard at Deptford, often called East Greenwich, Wells had the use there of a fine house with a spacious garden second in size and value only to the adjacent house reserved for his immediate superior, the Treasurer of the Navy. Here at Deptford Wells's associates were the high naval officers, the mariners who constantly brought back from distant lands data that would be scientifically valuable to anyone who could elicit and make use of it, and finally the naval architects from the adjacent shipyards. Among these master shipwrights would be Phineas Pett, Edward Stevens, Hugh Lydiard, and Henry Goddard, the father of the Jonathan Goddard who was one of the group mentioned by Wallis as meeting at Gresham College in 1645. Near by, also (after 1622, at least), would be John Clerke, who has already been mentioned in connection with Briggs and Bedwell, and was Keeper of the Armoury at Greenwich.

Most important, however, was the association of Wells and his naval friends with Briggs, Gunter, and Gellibrand, in turn. The State Papers carry no record of his association with Briggs, so here we must rely upon Wells's own statements. But certainly through such a man as Briggs's friend, Edward Wright, who was the foremost authority of the day on navigation, the Gresham professors would quickly be made acquainted with the navy group.

In Gunter's case, however, the State Papers give ample evidence of intimate association and collaboration with Wells and his shipwright friends. Gunter, Wells, Phineas Pett, Hugh Lydiard and Edward Stevens worked out together a more accurate method of calculating the tonnage of ships, and the State Papers for the years 1626 and 1628 are filled with records of their proofs of its superiority and of the campaign to secure its adoption.

After Gunter's death in December 1626, an equal intimacy sprang up between Wells and Gunter's successor at Gresham College, Henry Gellibrand. Gellibrand's most notable contribution to science was the proof of the secular variation of the magnetic needle – the 'variation of the variation'. Gellibrand, with Wells and several others, made the observations which led to the discovery of the secular variation in the garden of Wells's house at Deptford. There they repeated the observations that Wells and Gunter had made in the same place twelve years earlier, in 1622. Finding a difference of more than two degrees between his and Gunter's determination of the variation, and a difference of seven degrees between his determination and that made by William Borough in 1580, Gellibrand demonstrated that the variation near London had been gradually decreasing. . . .

The noted sea-captain and explorer Thomas James, whom we have already mentioned, should be added to this group of Gellibrand's friends and collaborators. Before James left on his famous voyage seeking the Northwest Passage, Gellibrand arranged with him to take simultaneous observations of the eclipse of the moon on October 29, 1631, Gellibrand at Gresham College and James wherever he might be in the northern regions of the New World. Gellibrand added 'An Appendix touching Longitude' to James's *Strange Voyage*, in which he compared the two sets of observations and from them calculated by a more exact mathematical method than would have otherwise been possible the precise longitude of James's position near Hudson's Bay.

The meetings and scientific investigations of Gellibrand and his associates at Gresham College and Deptford in the early 1630s contributed notably to the advancement of science. Could it be that Anthony Wood's statement that Gellibrand 'suffer'd conventicles (being himself a puritan) to be kept in his lodgings' at Gresham was based upon a report that confused these scientific gatherings with clandestine Puritan meetings? In view of the preponderantly Puritan sympathies of the members of the succeeding Gresham College group of the next decade, the supposition is at least plausible. An unostentatious assembly of a small group of men known to be of the Puritan party might well be suspected of having religion rather than scientific inquiry as its aim. . . .

Gellibrand's successor as Gresham Professor of Astronomy was Samuel Foster, in whose rooms Wallis first became acquainted with the group which he credits with being the 'first begetters' of the Royal Society. One member of this group was young Jonathan Goddard, one year junior to Wallis. Born in 1617 at East Greenwich in Kent, the son of Henry Goddard, John Wells's associate and close neighbour, Jonathan Goddard, after completing his studies at Cambridge, returned to London in 1640 to take up the practice of medicine. It is not surprising to find him, five years later, meeting with a group at Gresham College. When, in 1660, the Royal Society was established, Goddard had for five years been Gresham Professor of Physic.

Foster, in 1652, was succeeded by Lawrence Rooke, and it was in Rooke's, or Wren's rooms that the group was meeting in 1658 to 1660.

But Rooke, also, was from Deptford, where he was born in 1622, the year in which Gunter and Wells took observations on the magnetic variation in Wells's garden. His biographer states that, after receiving his M.A. at Cambridge in 1647, he retired to his estate in Kent, but in 1650 he went to Oxford and settled in Wadham College, for the sake of Dr Wilkins, who was then warden. But Wilkins did not go from London to Oxford until 1648, so that it is entirely possible that association with Wilkins in London, at the Gresham College gatherings, may have inspired Rooke to follow him to Oxford.

With this we bring to a close our narrative of the circle of scientific enthusiasts who gravitated about the successive Gresham professors during the half-century preceding the establishing of the Royal Society. In spite of the many obvious gaps in the evidence – gaps which research in English archives should some day remove –the outlines of the story stand out in clear relief. They picture a steady growth, from the very beginning of the seventeenth century, of association and collaboration among English scientists under the sponsorship of the Gresham professors of geometry and astronomy, and a close liaison throughout this period between the Gresham circle and prominent officials, captains, and shipbuilders of the English Navy. Without formal organization, but with the stability that only a secure and permanent foundation like that of Sir Thomas Gresham could supply, this circle, ever recruiting new members as the older ones passed on, entitles the Gresham College professors and their associates to the distinction of being named the true precursors of the Royal Society.

'Gresham College: Precursor of the Royal Society.'
Journal of the History of Ideas, 1940

IV

The Middle Ages

Medieval science still tends to be dismissed in textbooks as an unhappy blend of obscurantism and fable. Some historians use the words 'medieval' or 'Aristotelian' as a term of abuse. The work of Randall (p. 51) and Clagett (p. 40), however, make it difficult to do this today with any assurance. Randall has shown the strong claim which the Aristotelians of sixteenth-century Italy have to be regarded as the precursors of Galileo. Clagett, in profound and patient examination of the work of medieval theorists, much of it still in manuscript, has shown that much progress was made at this time. Lynn Thorndike (p. 36) points out that if medieval men were credulous, so also were the fellows of the Royal Society itself. If we tolerate superstition then, we must extend the same tolerance to the fourteenth century and not expect scientists to be entirely immune from the weaknesses of their period.

7 Aristotelianism in Renaissance Italy

J. H. RANDALL

The Aristotelian science which the thirteenth century had so eagerly worked into its Christian philosophy of life aimed at an understanding of nature divorced from power over things. But during the sixteenth century more men began to hold that science should be directed not merely to understanding and vision, but to a kind of understanding that might give power, action, and an improvement of the practical arts. A leading intellectual enterprise of the time was the search for a fruitful method that could serve this new aim to which knowledge was turning. Those thinkers whose energies were not wholly absorbed by the theological issues in terms of which the major battles were still being fought, concentrated on this problem of method as the paramount scientific task of the day.

Ironically enough, when the fruitful method was finally 'discovered' and proved in practice, it turned out to be the least novel of all the elements that went into the formation of the new science. After exploring many a blind alley, men came to realize that one of the great medieval intellectual traditions had already made an excellent beginning at just the kind of practical and useful knowledge they now wanted. In the thirteenth- and fourteenth-century schools, there had been worked out the idea of an experimentally grounded and mathematically formulated science of nature, and since then much had been done in the way of actual achievement. In Leonardo the penetrating, in the Italian mathematicians and physicists of the sixteenth century, in Copernicus, Kepler, and Galileo, such a science had indeed come of age.

Into this science there entered many different strands, each with its own history. And the powerful stimulus imparted during the sixteenth century by the recovery of the techniques of the Greek mathematicians is not to be minimized. But the conception of the nature of science, of its relation to the observations of fact, and of the method by which it might be achieved and formulated, that was handed on to his successors by Galileo, was not the work of the new seekers after a fruitful method. It appears rather as the culmination of the co-operative efforts of the generations of scientists inquiring into methodological problems in the universities of northern Italy. For three centuries the natural philosophers of the 'school of Padua' – which, *pace* Renan, should really be known as the 'School of Bologna and Padua', so close were the sister universities – in fruitful commerce with the physicians of their medical faculties, devoted themselves to criticizing and expanding this conception and method, and to grounding it firmly in the careful analysis of experience. It left their hands with a refinement and precision of statement which the seventeenth-century scientists who used it did not surpass in all their careful investigation of method.

In contrast with this cumulative and organized elaboration of the theory and method of science, the many humanist seekers, revolting from the 'scholasticism' of the Scotists and Ockhamites, with the technical 'terminist' logic, seem to have displayed all the customary ignorance and futility of intellectual revolutionaries, and to have proposed new methods distinguished chiefly by the novelty of their ignorance. As might be expected, these servants of the word for the most part sought their new method in language and in rhetoric, and tried to erect a 'natural dialectic' on the basis of Cicero and Quintilian. Others like Bruno were fascinated by the suggestions of Raymond Lull for a universal language that might reveal all truth. And still others, emphasizing the place of a knowledge of nature in human wisdom, urged men to close their books and observe the world.

The humanists might seek the method of a new science in the rhetorician's art of persuasion; a Luis Vives or a Francis Bacon, recognizing no useful knowledge in the investigations of the mathematicians and astronomers of their day, might counsel experience and ever more experience. Their combined onslaught helped to shake men's faith in the complacent academic traditionalism of the schools, already sorely disturbed by the new literary and theological movements; it hardly contributed much guidance to those already busily engaged upon scientific problems. Both in its traditional insights and in its novel guesses the imagination needed the discipline of a critical method before there could be any significant observation of facts. The body of ideas which in Galileo and Descartes dared to arrogate to itself the name of true 'natural philosophy', and which in Newton definitively made good that proud claim, had other and far deeper roots, stretching back through and beyond the twelfth-century European appropriation of ancient learning.

History has fallen into error in accepting uncritically the estimate the pioneer thinkers of the sixteenth and seventeenth centuries made of their own turning away from the heritage of the past. Their consciousness of fresh discovery and radical re-orientation obscured the countless bonds of continuity, in materials, methods, and even achievements, uniting them to their predecessors in the late Middle Ages. In particular the fact that the seventeenth-century scientists, in revolt against the humanists' appeal to the authority of the past, preferred to put their trust in 'natural reason' alone, and hence cared nothing for historical continuity, has sadly misled our judgement as to the fashion in which their thought was generated. Taking them at their own word, we have assumed that that co-operative criticism and reconstruction of a well-organized system of ideas, shaken from time to time by fresh insights which have had to be worked into the logical structure – that that process which has since the seventeenth century been so characteristic of the procedure of scientific advance – played no part in its earlier stages.

In the present generation much has been brought to light about the organized scientific traditions of the later Middle Ages in which the sixteenth- and seventeenth-century pioneers carried on their work. But much more remains to be done. In particular, the fact that several of the most influential investigators have been French has focused attention on the activities of the University of Paris, while the further fact that many of them have been Catholic scholars has made them not unduly appreciative of the work of the free-thinking and anti-clerical Italian schools. For its part, Italian scholarship has been attracted by the spectacular humanistic movement and by the presumably more novel and original literary Platonism of the Florentines. As a result, though it is clear that the thought of the Italian universities forms the immediate background of the sixteenth-century scientific movement that culminated in Galileo, its substantial achievement has as yet received almost no study.

The basic idea of an experimentally grounded science of the mathematical structure of nature appeared as soon as Europeans began to explore the wisdom of the ancients. It developed within the general framework of the first body of ancient materials to be assimilated, the Augustinian philosophy of reason – itself the platonized outcome of Hellenistic thought. It drew specifically upon the Arabic versions of Alexandrian science, though direct contact with the whole of Greek mathematics, astronomy, and mechanics was the last to be established; Archimedes was not known outside a narrow circle until the sixteenth century. But the idea of such a science and much of its method and concepts were in the possession of Europeans from the twelfth century on.

Aristotle's logic, his theory of science and method, was discovered in the *Analytics* during the first half of the twelfth century; his basic concepts and principles of natural science were learned from the *Physics* in the second half. The coming of Aristotle introduced a body of materials too impressive to be ignored. Thereafter for centuries the Aristotelian physical writings were taken as the starting point for all natural science, however far men might eventually depart from them; and the Aristotelian theory of science, however men might interpret it, remained dominant till the time of Newton. From the beginning of the fourteenth century, however, there set in a persistent and searching reconstruction of the Aristotelian tradition, which, when directed to the *Physics*, led by gradual stages to the mechanical and mathematical problems of the Galilean age, and when directed to the *Logic* led to the precise formulation of the method and structure of science acclaimed by all the seventeenth-century scientists.

There were two main critical movements during the later middle ages. The Ockhamites began in Oxford in the early fourteenth century, and while persisting there found a new stronghold during the next hundred years in the Faculty of Arts at Paris. The Latin Averroists began in Paris in the thirteenth century, and shifted their seat to Padua early in the fourteenth. Both set out by expressing a secular and anti-clerical spirit and by undertaking a destructive criticism of Thomism and Scotism, the thirteenth-century syntheses of science and religion. But both soon advanced beyond mere criticism to the constructive elaboration of natural science: they became the two great scientific schools of the later Middle Ages. The original work of the Ockhamites belongs to the fourteenth century, that of the Paduans, to the fifteenth and sixteenth. The former was done in dynamics, kinematics, and the logic of continuity and intensity; the latter in methodology and in the further development of dynamics. Both turned from the earlier religious syntheses to the purely natural philosophy of Aristotle himself; and both developed primarily by a constructive criticism of the Aristotelian texts and doctrines. The Ockhamites were at first the more 'progressive' and 'modern'; they were interested in the free develop-ment of the Aristotelian physics, and their works take the form of *questions* and *problems* suggested by Aristotle's analyses. The Averroists, though much more secular and anti-clerical, were originally more conservative in their attitude towards Aristo le and his interpreter Averroes: their works are characteristically *commentaries* on the texts. From 1400 on, however, they knew and taught all the Ockhamite departures from Aristotelian doctrine: Paul of Venice (died 1429) is remarkably up to date, and his *Summa Naturalis* contains an exposition of all the ideas of the dynamics of the Paris Ockhamites and the Oxford logicians. The works of these fourteenth-century thinkers were printed in many editions so soon as the press reached Italy, all of them by 1490; and in the sixteenth century it was primarily the Italians who advanced by successive stages to the formulations of Galileo.

About 1400, therefore, the interest in the development of scientific ideas shifts from Ockhamite Paris to the Padua Averroists. From the time of Paul of Venice to Cremonini (died 1631) the Aristotelian physics and a nascent 'Galilean' physics were in definite and conscious opposi-tion at Padua, and this critical conflict contributed greatly to the working out of the latter. Paul of Venice had been sent by his order to Oxford in 1390, where he remained for three years; he then taught for two more in Paris at the time of the last great Ockhamite, Pierre d'Ailly. He thus knew all the Ockhamite developments at first hand, and explained them fully though critically in his encyclopedic writings.

His successor at Padua, Cajetan of Thiene (died 1465), was the most radical scientifically of the Averroists, and the most sympathetic to the Paris teachings on dynamics. He initiated a great controversy over the *Calculations* of Suisseth (Swineshead), in which all the arguments for a mathematical as against a qualitative controversy, in many editions, were among the first works printed in Italy in the 1480s. The fundamental *De latitudinibus formarum* of Nicholas of Oresme, in which the rule for uniformly accelerated motion first appears, came out in 1482, with a discussion by Blasius de Parma de Pelicanis; Albert of Saxony's *Tractatus de proportionibus*, arguing for a quantitative treatment of qualities (already reported in the *Summa Naturalis* of Paul of Venice) also appeared in the same year; in 1496 it was reprinted with the *De Intensione et Remissione formarum* of Walter Burleigh, a defence of the logic of qualitative change opposed to the spirit of Oresme, and with a full reply to Burleigh on behalf of quantitative analysis by the physician Jacopo da Forli. Among the most interesting of all these documents, indicative of a lively concern with what was to become the fundamental scientific question, is the *Tractatus de Proportionibus* of a Milanese physician, Johannes Marlianus (Pavia, 1482), which brings experimental proof to bear on the quantitative side, describes the rolling of balls down an inclined plane to measure their velocity and acceleration, and narrates experiments with pendulums.

The question of whether the operation of causes was to be formulated mathematically or qualitatively (whether the 'first accident' of substance was to be taken as quantity or not – which happens to be also the way in which Kepler expressed his view that a cause is a mathematical law) was thus vigorously debated at Padua towards the end of the fifteenth century, and the notion of 'cause' as a mathematically formulated cause won many adherents. In the next century there broke out another great controversy among the Paduans as to whether the 'cause' of natural motion was to be sought in a form or in a force, that is, in a definite way of behaving or in something that acted in a definite way. Galileo joined those who identified 'cause' with a 'force'; but since he also defined force in terms of its way of acting, his divergence was not great. And towards the end of the same century there occurred another dispute, as to whether final causes had any place in natural philosophy. The outcome of these successive debates was to delimit the conception of 'cause', and to make the Galilean position inevitable. They are here mentioned to suggest certain other strands in the development of Italian Aristotelianism which this study does not presume to set forth in detail, and which in particular illuminate the change from a qualitative to a mathematical treatment of natural operations.

It has become a recent fashion to view the whole 'Renaissance', and indeed the very 'birth' of modern science itself, as, philosophically, a turning from the Aristotle of the Schools to Platonism; and Italian thought of the fifteenth century has been seen as dominated by that turning. But it must not be forgotten that the vigorous intellectual life of the Italian universities remained loyal to the Aristotelian tradition. Now in most countries the fifteenth century saw the teaching and refinement of the earlier philosophies, Scotism, Thomism, and Ockhamism, with little basically new. But in northern Italy, at Padua, Bologna, and Pavia, and to a lesser extent at Siena, Pisa, and the brilliant new university of Ferrara, Aristotelianism was still a living and growing body of ideas. What Paris had been in the thirteenth century, what Oxford became in the fifteenth, the centre in which ideas from all Europe were combined into an organized and cumulative body of knowledge. A succession of great teachers carried that knowledge to the point where in the next century it could find fruitful marriage with the new interest in the mathematical sciences. In the Italian schools alone the emerging science of nature did not mean a sharp break with reigning theological interests. To them it came rather as the natural outcome of a sustained and co-operative criticism of Aristotelian ideas. If in the sixteenth century the more original minds were led to a formal break with the Padua teaching, we must not forget that even Galileo occupied a chair there from 1592 to 1610, and that in method and philosophy if not in physics he remained a typical Padua Aristotelian.

That Italian Aristotelianism was thus able to lead the European schools in the fifteenth and sixteenth centuries was due to several circumstances, not the least of which was the settled commercial prosperity the Italian cities had now achieved. They had long enjoyed and taught in their universities a thoroughly secular and largely anti-clerical philosophy expressive of the new culture of a this-worldly and commercial society. By 1400 that nice blend of Aristotelian science and Christian faith which Thomas and Duns Scotus had constructed had, in Italy at least, retreated into the monastic orders. At Padua, Bologna and Pavia there reigned an Aristotelianism that made little attempt to accommodate itself to theological interests. And it is no accident that while the Church-controlled science of the North drove all those who felt the new currents into open rebellion against 'science' itself, the anti-clerical science of the Italian universities could progress steadily in self-criticism to the achievement of a Galileo.

Fundamental also was the close alliance between the study of Aristotle and the study of medicine.... At Padua the Faculty of Arts led primarily to that of Medicine, and Aristotle was there taught as a preparation, not for an ecclesiastical career, but for the study of medicine, with a consequent strong emphasis on his physical writings, his natural history, and his scientific methodology. The Theological Faculty at Padua was never able to exert much influence on the others. A physician's Aristotle is bound to differ from a theologian's. The teachers wrote no theological works, no commentaries on the *Sentences*. They normally held medical degrees themselves; they applied Aristotle to medical problems, and to questions of method arising in medical science; they interpreted him in the light of the best medical writers of the Greek and Arabic tradition.

Finally, the liberty of teaching and speculation guaranteed by Venice, the leading Italian anti-papal and anti-clerical state, after its acquisition of Padua in 1405, attracted the best minds from all over Italy, especially the philosophical Southerners. Padua remained to the days of Galileo the leading scientific school of Europe, the stronghold of the Aristotelian qualitative physics, and the trainer even of those who were to break with it. Cusanus, Peurbach, Regiomontanus, Copernicus, as well as the Italians, all studied at Padua.

If the concepts of a mathematical physics were arrived at by a long criticism of Aristotelian ideas, the 'new method', the logic and methodology taken over and expressed by Galileo and destined to become the scientific method of the seventeenth-century physicists, as contrasted with the many noisy proposals of the sixteenth-century 'buccinators' down to Francis Bacon, was even more clearly the result of a fruitful science, undertaken at Padua in particular, and fertilized by the methodological discussions of the commentators on the medical writers. For three hundred years, after Pietro d'Abano brought the problems to the fore, the Padua medical teachers were driven by their texts, especially Galen, to a careful analysis of scientific procedure. The great commentators on Galen, Jacopo da Forli (died 1413), who, incidentally, wrote widely on the methods of the Paris physicists, and Hugo of Siena (Ugo Benzi, died 1439), gradually built up a detailed theory of scientific method which the Aristotelian scholars, themselves holders of medical degrees, incorporated into their version of the nature of science. It is possible to trace step by step in rather beautiful fashion the gradual elaboration of the Aristotelian method, in the light of the medical tradition, from its first discussion in Pietro d'Abano to its completed statement in the logical controversies of Zabarella, in which it reaches the form familiar in Galileo and the seventeenth-century scientists.

. . . The originality of Zabarella, and of the whole development of which he is the culmination, is thus to set off a 'scientific experience' from mere ordinary observation, the accidental or planless collection of particular cases. The weakness of the logic of the Schoolmen had lain precisely in their acceptance of first principles established by mere common observation. In contrast, Zabarella, and with him the whole new science, insisted that experience must first be analysed carefully to discover the precise 'principle' or cause of the observed effects, the universal structure involved in them. After this analytic way of discovery had been pursued, we are then in a position to demonstrate deductively how facts follow from this principle or cause: we can pursue the way of truth. Scientific method, that is, proceeds from the rigorous analysis of a few selected instances or illustrations to a general principle, and then goes from that principle back to the systematic and ordered body of facts, to the science itself formally expressed. Zabarella calls this the combination of the resolutive and the compositive methods; and such were precisely the procedure and the terms of Galileo. The presupposition of this method is of course that there exists an intelligible structure in the subject-matter under examination, of which the particular cases observed by the senses are instances; Zabarella makes this perfectly plain.

> 'Demonstrative induction can be carried on in a necessary subject-matter, and in things that have an essential connection with each other. Hence it does not take all the particulars into account, since after certain of them have been examined our mind straightway notices the essential connection, and then disregarding the remaining particulars proceeds at once to bring together the universal. For it knows that it is necessary that the same relations should be embodied in the rest.'

No clearer statement could be made of the procedure of the seventeenth-century scientists.

It is not surprising that Galileo should so often sound like Zabarella. For he arrived in Padua in 1592, while the echoes of the great controversies over method between Zabarella on the one hand and Francesco Piccolomini and his disciple Petrella on the other, fought in the 1580s, were still resounding – controversies of which a witness has recorded: 'The school of logic at Padua was divided into two sects, those who were partisans of Zabarella, and those who were partisans of Petrella, and a multitude seemed to stand on either side. After this most exalted and famous controversy, so useful and fruitful to all students of logic, both published commentaries on the *Posterior Analytics*; than which commentaries, though they were different, and contain divergent teaching, in the common judgement of learned men nothing can be found more exquisite or more clear.'

In these two controversies, the points at issue were relatively minor in comparison with the bulk of agreement on method. Piccolomini, an older man, holder of the first chair of natural philosophy since 1564, had come to Padua from Siena, bringing a certain Platonism with his Aristotelianism; but though he defends some Platonic positions, on method he is as advanced as Zabarella, and as near to the ideas of the seventeenth-century scientists. He agrees on the central importance of resolution as the way of discovery. But against his demand that metaphysics must furnish the starting point and frame of reference in all science, and that the scientist must imitate the fixed structure of nature, Zabarella maintains the independence and self-sufficiency of natural science, and indeed of each particular subject-matter, making the end of knowledge and inquiry a human thing, and directing the sciences towards human goals and aims. He defends the knowledge given by induction as perfect in its own kind, the constitution of man being what it is; it is no mere substitute for something that might be better gained in a more perfect way. And against Piccolomini's Platonic conception of a natural order of perfections which science must follow, he maintains a purely immanent conception of natural ends: the perfect functioning of each kind of thing in the universe is its only end, and each subject-matter is to be understood in terms of its own principles. Indeed, in his criticisms of Platonic notions of teleology Zabarella went far along the path the earlier pupil of Paduans, Telesio, had already taken.

Zabarella's version of the Aristotelian logic, though interpreted and coloured in terms of each of the three great theories of knowledge inherited and reconstructed by the seventeenth-century thinkers, and though receiving in practice wide variations of emphasis on its several parts, remained the method and ideal of science for all 'natural philosophers' until the fresh criticisms of Locke and Berkeley. For though the language is diverse, the whole great literature on method that fills the scientific writing of the seventeenth century is at bottom a series of footnotes to the *Organon* of Aristotle. Indeed, the more fully the record of late medieval and Renaissance thought is studied, the clearer it becomes that the most daring departures from Aristotelian science were carried on within the Aristotelian framework, and by means of a critical reflection on the Aristotelian texts – however various the sources the ideas that fertilized that criticism. The 'father' of modern science, in fact, turns out to be none other than the Master of them that know.

With Zabarella the Padua school had reached its culmination and done its work. His single successor, Cesare Cremonini (died 1631), went still farther in an appeal to experience. His *Tractatus de Paedia* (1596) sounds like the solemn warning of the great tradition of Aristotelian rational empiricism to the triumphant mathematicians.

'*Paedia* is the power of judging rightly about the manner of teaching and learning, founded on logic, with the opportune intervention of experience . . . Its intrinsic function is to understand, dispose, and constitute the general method of all procedures. As *Paedia* is the mother and nurse, so is method the daughter and child. I add, "with the intervention of experience", because, though one be instructed by genius or by logic, unless he be also experienced in the very thing in which he is to judge, he will there exercise no judgement. I say "opportune", or appropriate, because the same manner of experience is not found everywhere. In mathematics, for the confirming of principles it is sufficient to employ induction based on the observation of what is in the materials whence mathematics is abstracted; in that field the truth of the principle is immediately evident. But in the natural sciences such observation is not so obvious a way of gaining principles, nor is the collection of principles by its employment so easy. There is indeed required a laborious attention procured from a zealous application to things; and even with it the principles are arrived at not without keen thought. Moreover, this experience is necessary not only for the natural scientist, if he is to arrive at first principles; it is requisite for almost every manner of science. For experience is likewise required in morals in much the same fashion, and even in divinity, since we do not ascend to these abstract causes without a manifold and laborious attention to their effects.'

And so he counselled ever closer attention to the way of discovery, to the careful and painstaking analysis of experience, to the method of resolution, within which he included as phases both induction and demonstration *a posteriori*.

There was but one element lacking in Zabarella's formulation of method; he did not insist that the principles of natural science be mathematical, and indeed drew his illustrations largely from Aristotle's biological subject-matter. Though he had studied mathematics under Catena and Barocius, and was accounted expert in optics and in astronomy, these fields failed to leave any fundamental impress on his thought. The gradual emergence of mathematics into the dominant position it held in the seventeenth century is due to its cultivation by a small group of men working on the periphery of the main intellectual movements of the sixteenth century. There is a conventional view that this shift to mathematical interests was powerfully furthered by the Renaissance revival of Platonism and its number mysticism, derived from Proclus, from the Pythagorean tradition, and from the Cabala. In the Germanies this has some basis of fact, and Kepler may stand as its consummation. But it is difficult to find any support for the view that attributes the great achievements of the Italians in mathematics and mechanics to the influence of neoplatonism. On the one hand the Italian Platonists had almost no scientific interest in mathematics, and their 'numbers' led them at once to the mazes of theology and theosophy. Only Cardano and Patrizzi among the Platonists had scientific interests. And on the other, with rare exceptions the Italian mathematicians down through Galileo, when they possessed a philosophical interest at all, were not Platonists but Aristotelians in their view of mathematics, of its relations to physics, and of the proper method of natural knowledge. What they found in the ancients and what they worked upon themselves was no mathematical vision of the world, but effective techniques and practical problems of procedure and discovery. What they constructed as 'new sciences' it remained for Descartes to interpret in the light of the tradition of Augustinian Platonism.

Indeed, the one contribution the Humanists can fairly claim to have made to the rise of modern science was to send men to the study of the original ancient sources in mathematics. In re-establishing connection with the mathematics and mechanics of the Hellenistic age, the appeal to the ancients introduced Archimedes and Hero, as well as Apollonius, Pappus and Diophantus. The mathematical methods of analysis and synthesis of Archimedes, of whom Tartaglia published the first Latin edition in 1543, were the one element which neither the fourteenth-century Ockhamites nor the sixteenth-century Paduans possessed. From them the mathematicians took their start, and carried the day for the quantitative side of the Padua discussion, to which reference has been made above.

With this mathematical emphasis added to the logical methodology of Zabarella, there stands completed the 'new method' for which men had been so eagerly seeking. By the analysis of the mathematical relations involved in a typical 'effect' or phenomenon we arrive at its formal structure or 'principle'. From that principle we deduce further consequences, which we find illustrated and confirmed in experience. Science is a body of mathematical demonstrations, the principles of which are discovered by the resolution of selected instances in experience. This is the method called by Euclid and Archimedes a combination of 'analysis' and 'synthesis', and by the Paduans and Galileo, 'resolution' and 'composition'.

This method is traditional and Aristotelian in regarding the structure of science as dialectical and deductive, and in seeing all verification and demonstration as inclusion within a logical system of ideas. It has altered the scheme of the medieval Aristotelians in making the principles of demonstration mathematical in character; and to the scholastic empiricism it has added the insistence that the way of discovery is not mere observation and generalization, not mere abstraction from common experience, but a careful and precise mathematical analysis of a scientific experience – what the medical tradition of Padua called 'resolution' and what Archimedes called 'analysis'. And to that experience demonstration must return in a 'regress' for confirmation, illustration, and the guarantee of the existence of the deduced consequences. But the return to experience is not for the sake of certain proof: for throughout the seventeenth century it is almost impossible to find any natural scientist maintaining that a mere fact can prove any certain truth.

The School of Padua and the Emergence of Modern Science
Editrice Antenore: Padua 1961
pp. 15–67

V

Social and Religious Considerations

A good deal of controversy has been engendered on the relative importance of theory and practice in the history of science. Engels's letter of 1894 (p. 64) may be taken as expressing succinctly the typical Marxist approach to this problem. This point of view has been defended and maintained many times. Zilsel's article (p. 86) may stand as an example of the work of historians who stress sociological considerations as the main explanation of the Scientific Revolution. The article by Rupert Hall (p. 67) may be taken as a balanced criticism of this point of view. Randall (p. 51) stresses the importance of universities, a point supported so far as England is concerned by the recent book of Professor Mark Curtis, Oxford and Cambridge in Transition. The American sociologist R. K. Merton regarded the role of Puritanism as being of crucial importance in the rise of science. His work is not represented here but a similar point is made by S. F. Mason (p. 100).

8 A Marxist View

ENGELS TO STARKENBURG

London, January 25, 1894

Dear Sir,

Here is the answer to your questions:

1. What we understand by the economic relations, which we regard as the determining basis of the history of society, is the manner and method by which human beings in a given society, produce their means of subsistence and exchange the products among themselves (in so far as division of labour exists). Thus the *entire technique* of production and transport is here included. According to our conception this

technique also determines the manner and method of exchange and, further, the distribution of products and with it, after the dissolution of gentile society, also the division into classes, and hence the relations of lordship and servitude and with them the state, politics, law, etc. Further included in economic relations are the *geographical basis* on which they operate and those remnants of earlier stages of economic development which have actually been transmitted and have survived – often only through tradition or by force of inertia; also of course the external environment which surrounds this form of society.

If, as you say, technique largely depends on the state of science, science depends far more still on the *state* and the *requirements* of technique. If society has a technical need, that helps science forward more than ten universities. The whole of hydrostatics (Torricelli, etc.) was called forth by the necessity for regulating the mountain streams of Italy in the sixteenth and seventeenth centuries. We have only known anything reasonable about electricity since its technical applicability was discovered. But unfortunately it has become the custom in Germany to write the history of the sciences as if it had fallen from the skies.

2. We regard economic conditions as the factor which ultimately conditions historical development. But race is itself an economic factor. Here, however, two points must not be overlooked:

(*a*) Political, juridical, philosophical, religious, literary, artistic, etc., development is based on economic development. But all these react upon one another and also upon the economic basis. It is not that the economic condition is the *cause* and *alone active*, while everything else only has a passive effect. There is, rather, interaction on the basis of economic necessity, which *ultimately* always asserts itself. The state, for instance, exercises an influence by protective tariffs, free trade, good or bad fiscal system; and even the deadly inanimation and impotence of the German philistine, arising from the miserable economic condition of Germany from 1648 to 1830 and expressing itself at first in pietism, then in sentimentality and cringing servility to princes and nobles, was not without economic effect. It was one of the greatest hindrances to recovery and was not shaken until the revolutionary and Napoleonic wars made the chronic misery an acute one. So it is not, as people try here and there conveniently to imagine, that the economic condition produces an automatic effect. No, men make their history themselves, only they do so in a given environment which conditions it and on the basis of actual relations already existing, among which the economic relations, however much they may be influenced by the other – political and ideological – ones, are still ultimately the decisive ones, forming the red thread which runs through them and alone leads to understanding.

(*b*) Men make their history themselves, but not as yet with a collective will according to a collective plan or even in a definite, delimited given society. Their aspirations clash, and for that very reason all such societies are governed by *necessity*, which is complemented by and appears under the forms of *accident*. The necessity which here asserts itself athwart all accident is again ultimately economic necessity. This is where the so-called great men come in for treatment. That such and such a man and precisely that man arises at a particular time in a particular country is, of course, pure chance. But cut him out and there will be a demand for a substitute, and this substitute will be found, good or bad, but in the long run he will be found. That Napoleon, just that particular Corsican, should have been the military dictator whom the French Republic, exhausted by its own warfare, had rendered necessary, was chance; but that, if a Napoleon had been lacking, another would have filled the place, is proved by the fact that the man was always found as soon as he became necessary: Caesar, Augustus, Cromwell, etc. While Marx discovered the materialist conception of history, Thierry, Mignet, Guizot and all the English historians up to 1850 are the proof that it was being striven for, and the discovery of the same conception by Morgan proves that the time was ripe for it and that it simply *had* to be discovered.

So with all the other accidents, and apparent accidents, of history. The further the particular sphere which we are investigating is removed from the economic sphere and approaches that of pure abstract ideology, the more shall we find it exhibiting accidents in its development, the more will its curve run in a zigzag. But if you plot the average axis of the curve, you will find that the axis of this curve will run more and more nearly parallel to the axis of the curve of economic development, the longer the period considered and the wider the field dealt with.

KARL MARX and F. ENGELS: *Selected Works*
Lawrence and Wishart 1951
vol. ii., pp. 457–79

9 The Scholar and the Craftsman

A. R. HALL

Never has there been such a time as that during the later sixteenth and the seventeenth centuries for the great diversity of men in the forefront of scientific achievement. A proportion of those who contributed to the swelling literature of science were in a broad sense professionals: indeed, a sizeable proportion, since many minor figures enlarge this group. Among these professionals were university teachers, professors of mathematics, anatomy, and medicine; teachers of these subjects especially applied mathematics, outside the universities; and their various practitioners – physicians, surveyors, mariners, engineers and so on; and lastly the instrument-makers, opticians, apothecaries, surgeons, and other tradesmen, though their great period in science is to be found rather in the eighteenth century than in the seventeenth. These men, widely divergent as they were in social origins and intellectual attainments, at least occupied positions in a recognizable scientific hierarchy. Some had won them through academic study, others through private education and research, others again by apprenticeship and pursuit of an occupation closely related to scientific inquiry. All were trained men in some way, whether in mathematics, physic and dissection, or the exercise of a manual craft. Now it is surprising enough, whether we make comparison with the scientific world of recent times or with that of the later Middle Ages, we find such disparity in the professional group, that is, to find that the definition of scientific professionalism must be so loosely drawn; yet it is still more astonishing that many minor figures in the history of seventeenth-century science, and not a few notable ones, constitute an even more heterogeneous collection. Among these true 'amateurs' of science (the distinction has really little meaning), some, it is true, had been exposed to scientific influences of a kind in college or university; yet the creation of a permanent interest thus, in an ordinary passing student, must have been as rare then as the acquisition of a taste for Latin verse is now. A few also, no doubt, were quietly encouraged by discerning fathers or by private patrons. The rest remain as 'sports'; diffusionist and environmental principles hardly suffice to explain their appearance on the scene. One thinks of such men as William Petty, son of a clothier, Otto von Guericke, Mayor of Magdeburg, John

Flamsteed, an independent gentleman of modest means, or, most extraordinary of all, Antony van Leeuwenhoek, an unschooled borough official.

Thus one can never predict the social circumstances or personal history of a seventeenth-century scientist. Given the taste, the ability and freedom from the immediate necessities of the struggle for subsistence, any man who could read and write might become such. Latin was no longer essential, nor mathematics, nor wide knowledge of books, nor a professorial chair. Publication in journals, even membership in scientific societies, was open to all; no man's work needed the stamp of academic approval. This was the free age between the medieval M.A. and the modern Ph.D. In the virtual absence of systematic scientific training, when far more was learned from books than from lectures, the wholly self-educated man was hardly at a disadvantage as compared with his more fortunate colleague who had attended the seats of learning, except perhaps in such special fields as theoretical astronomy or human anatomy. There were no important barriers blocking entry into the newer areas of exploration, such as chemistry, microscopy, qualitative astronomy, where all types of ability, manual and intellectual, were almost equally required. Obviously it was statistically more probable that a scientist would spring from the gentry class (if I may use this disputed term) than any other, and that he would be a university man rather than not. But the considerations determining the probability were sociological rather than scientific; if the texture of science was almost infinitely receptive of first-rate ability of any kind, the texture of society was such that it was more likely to emerge from some quarters than from others.

It is needful to traverse this familiar ground in order to set in perspective the dichotomy to which I shall turn – that of craftsman and scholar. It is a quadruple dichotomy – social, intellectual, teleological, and educational. It marks off, broadly, men of one class in society from another – those who earn their bread from scientific trades of one kind or another from those who do not. It distinguishes likewise those achievements in science which are in the main practical or operational from those which are cerebral or conceptual. Thirdly, it draws attention to the different objects of those who seek mainly practical success through science, and those who seek mainly understanding. And finally, if we consider only the group whom I have previously called professional, we may discern on the one hand the 'scholars' who have been introduced to science by university or similar studies, and on the other the 'craftsmen' who have learnt something of practical science in a trade. But we must be cautious in detecting polar opposites where there is in reality a spectrum. The scientific movement of the seventeenth century was infinitely varied, its successes demanded an infinite range of different qualities, and it is against this background of wide inclusion that we must set any attempt at analysis in particular terms.

By far the most closely-knit, homogeneous, and intellectually influential of the groups I have described was that of the university men, including both those who remained as teachers and those who departed to other walks of life. Some of the harshest critics of the contemporary 'schools', like Bacon, Descartes, or Webster, were nevertheless their products. The opponents of the Aristotelian 'forms and qualities' had been firmly grounded in that doctrine; many future scientists found stimulus in the universally required mathematical studies. To exemplify this point, one may consider the earliest membership of the Royal Society in 1663. Of the 115 names listed, I find that 65 had definitely attended a university, while only 16 were certainly non-academic. The remaining 34 are doubtful, but at any rate the university men had the majority. It is still more telling to single out the names which have a definite association-value on inspection; I rate 38 on this test, of whom 32 are 'U' and only 6 non-'U'. Whether or not we term such men 'scholars' is largely a rather unimportant question of definition: at any rate they had in common a knowledge of Latin, some training in mathematics, and an introduction at least to logic, and natural philosophy; quite a proportion would also have had such experience of the biological and medical sciences as was available at the time.

It appears then that the medieval association of scientific activity with the universities was weakened, but not disrupted, in the seventeenth century, though the association certainly became less strong as the century advanced. It was weakened not only by the importance in science of men who were not academically trained at all, but by the shift in the locus of scientific activity from the universities, where it had remained securely fixed throughout the Middle Ages, to new institutions like Gresham College, to the scientific societies meeting in capital cities, and to the circles basking in the patronage of a Montmor or a Medici. If a majority of creative scientists had been at the university, they were so no longer in their mature age. Moreover, while in the medieval university there had been little disparity between the instruction given to the student, and the advanced researches of the master, this was no longer the case in the seventeenth century. In the schools of the fourteenth century the master who remained to teach pushed forward his knowledge, in the main, within the framework of ideas, and through study of authorities, with which he had become familiar at a more elementary level. The seventeenth-century university, on the other hand, almost ignored observational and experimental science. The unprecedented advances in scientific technique occurring in physics, astronomy, botany and zoology, and chemistry were not made widely available to students: there was a fairly good grounding only in mathematics and human medicine. The potential investigator had to learn the techniques he required from practice, by the aid of books, and through personal contact with an experienced scientist, often only obtainable elsewhere. Perhaps even more serious was the absence from university courses of the leading principles of the scientific revolution and of the ideas of the new natural philosophy. In the last quarter of the seventeenth century Cartesian science was indeed expounded in some of the colleges of France, and less widely elsewhere, but dissemination of the thought of Galileo, of Bacon, and of the exponents of the mechanical philosophy owed little to university courses. Occasional examples of a university teacher having a decided influence upon a circle of pupils – as was the case with John Wilkins at Wadham College, Oxford, and Isaac Barrow at Trinity, Cambridge – hardly vitiate the general conclusion that the activities of various societies, books, and journals were far more potent vehicles of proselytization, which is supported by many personal biographies. However stimulating the exceptional teacher, formal courses were commonly conservative and pedestrian: it is curious to note that the two greatest scientists of the age who were also professors, Galileo and Newton, seem to have been singularly unremarkable in their public instruction. If the universities could produce scholars, they were ill-adapted to turning out scientists; the scientist had to train himself. Many who accomplished this transition regarded it, indeed, as a revulsion from the ordinary conception of scholarship. The learning they genuinely prized, in their own scientific disciplines, they had hardly won for themselves. It would surely be absurd to argue that Newton was less a self-made scientist than Huyghens, or Malpighi than Leeuwenhoek, because the former had attended a university and the latter not.

It lies outside my brief to discuss the fossilization of the universities, which, from what I can learn, the Renaissance did little to diminish so far as science was concerned, nor the rise of the new science as a rejection of academic dogma. Recent investigations would, I believe, tend to make one hesitant in concluding that the innovations and criticisms in the academic sciences – astronomy, physics, anatomy – which we call the scientific revolution, were the product solely, or even chiefly, of forces and changes operating outside the universities. Rather it would seem that, in relation to these subjects, it was a case of internal strife, one party of academic innovators trying to wrest the field from a more numerous one of academic conservatives. Certainly this was the case with Vesalius and his fellow-anatomists, with Copernicus, with Galileo. It was the academic and professional world that was passionately divided on the question of the inviolability of the Galenic, Aristotelian, or Ptolemaic doctrines; these quarrels of learned men had as little to do with capitalism as with the protestant ethic. Only towards the middle of the seventeenth century were they extended through the wider range of the educated class.

In the long run – that is to say within a century or so in each instance – the innovators won. In the short run they were defeated; academic conservatism prevented the recognition and implementation of the victories of the revolution in each science until long after they were universally applauded by thoughtful men outside. Whereas in the thirteenth century the schools had swung over to the Greeks and Muslims despite their paganism and their often unorthodox philosophy, whereas in the fourteenth century the development of mechanics, of astronomy theoretical and practical, of anatomical and other medical studies had been centred upon them, in the sixteenth and seventeenth centuries teaching failed to adapt itself to the pace with which philosophy and science were moving. In the mid-sixteenth century the universities could still have formed the spearhead of this astonishing intellectual advance, in Galileo's lifetime the opportunity was lost, and despite the invaluable efforts of individual teachers, as institutions the universities figured only in the army of occupation, a fantastic position not reversed until the nineteenth century. The innovators really failed, at the critical period, to capture the universities and bring them over to their side as centres of teaching and research in the new scientific manner. There were, for instance, many schemes in the seventeenth century for organizing scientific research, and for the provision of observatories, museums, laboratories and so on; yet no one, I think, thought of basing such new institutions on a university. That would have seemed, during the last century, a natural course to follow; and it would presumably have seemed equally natural in the Middle Ages.

Hence it happened that the academic type, the scholar, book-learned in Aristotle or Galen, the Simplicius, the professor who could see the holes in the septum of the heart but was blind to the spots on the face of the sun, became the butt of the scientific revolutionaries.

> Oxford and Cambridge are our laughter,
> Their learning is but pedantry,

as the ballad has it. The passage in the *Discourse on Method* may be recalled, in which Descartes reviews critically the content of education and learning as ordinarily understood:

> 'Of philosophy I will say nothing, except that when I saw it had been cultivated for many ages by the most distinguished men, and that yet there is not a single matter within its sphere which is not still in dispute, and nothing therefore which is above doubt, I did not presume to anticipate that my success would be greater in it than that of others, and further, when I considered the number of conflicting opinions touching a single matter that may be upheld by learned men, while there can be but one true, I reckoned as well-nigh false all that was only probable.'

After observing that the other sciences derived their principles from philosophy, which was itself infirm, so that 'neither the honour nor the gain held out by them was sufficient to determine one to their cultivation', Descartes abandoned the study of letters 'and resolved no longer to seek any other science than the knowledge of myself, or of the great book of the world'. With this one may compare Bacon's 'surprise, that among so many illustrious colleges in Europe, all the foundations are engrossed by the professions, none being left for the free cultivation of the arts and sciences'. This restriction, he declares, 'has not only dwarfed the growth of the sciences, but been prejudicial to states and governments themselves'. The candid appraisal of the first chapter of the *Advancement of Learning* could have been applied to many academic institutions more than two centuries after it was penned.

Admittedly the period when Bacon and Descartes formed such adverse opinions was one early in the scientific revolution; but there is little evidence to show that academic reform progressed rapidly thereafter, and it would not be difficult to quote parallel judgements from a later time. It was not the case, of course, that learned conservatives could see no merit in the study of science. This was no science-versus-humanities wrangle, for the conservatives were themselves teachers of science, of Renaissance science in fact. Their science was Aristotelian and formal; it denounced both Copernicanism and the mechanical philosophy, and distrusted the new instruments and experiments. An analogous situation existed in medicine, where the modernists who were experimenting with chemical preparations and new drugs such as a guaiacum and Jesuits' bark, who followed Harvey and attempted the transfusion of blood, were opposed by the entrenched faculties of so-called Galenists, enemies of every innovation. Nevertheless, the effect was much the same: The 'new philosophy' and science were forced to take root outside the academic garden where they should have found most fertile soil.

The effect of the development of new scientific ideas and methods in diminishing the role of the universities as creative centres reinforced rather than initiated the decline of their intellectual prestige, which had begun with the Renaissance. Then, too, new movements in learning and scholarship were at least as much associated with the activities of private scholars, as with those of university teachers. Private patrons had been as energetic in encouraging neo-classical modes of writing and sculpture, as they were to be in promoting science in the seventeenth century. Already in the Renaissance academic learning was reproached for its inelegance in the classical tongues, its imported Arabisms, its lingering attachment to imperfect texts, its barren philosophy. No one was more scathing of academic pedantry than Erasmus, not to say Paracelsus. 'Then grew the learning of the schoolmen to be utterly despised as barbarous', says Bacon, so that when he himself attacked the fine philosophic web of scholasticism – too many words spun out of too little matter – he was but repeating an old canard. This revulsion of the Renaissance scholar from the 'barbarousness' of still-medieval universities was, as is well known, a linguistic and textual one in the main; it did not touch so much the content of thought as its expression, nor did it, in particular, greatly disturb the pre-eminent position of the ancient masters of science. This aspect of the Renaissance can most clearly be seen in the history of medicine during the first half of the sixteenth century. Some of the lost ground the universities recovered; they began to teach Greek and Ciceronian Latin; more attention was paid to history and literature and less to disputative philosophy. But they could not recover their medieval pre-eminence as cultural centres – particularly perhaps in northern Europe – and the scientists of the seventeenth century had only, in a sense, to follow the path which Renaissance humanists had trodden, in rejecting it.

The object of the preceding remarks is to justify my conception of the scientific scholar of the sixteenth and seventeenth centuries, as a man learned not merely in recent scientific activities and methods, but in the thought of the past. It seems superfluous to argue that the majority of the scientists of the time were of this type, neither technicians nor ignorant empiricists. Certainly the learning of Galileo, or Mersenne, of Huyghens, or Newton, was not quite like the learning in the medieval or Renaissance conception; they may have been as deficient in the subtleties of Thomist philosophy as in the niceties of the Greek syntax; but to deny that they were learned scholars in their field and in their outlook would be to deny that any scientist is entitled to be called learned.

I have tried also to trace in outline the way in which, at this time, scientific learning diverged from other branches of scholarship, without wholly severing its affiliation with academic institutions. One might also ask the question: how far was the new scientific spirit of the seventeenth century brought into being by activities of a purely scholarly kind – for example, through the evolution of certain principles of logic during the Middle Ages, or through the activities of the persistent students of Greek science in the Renaissance?

The latter especially furnished the core of an interpretation of the scientific revolution which held favour until recent times. To put it crudely, the scientific revolution was seen, according to this view, as the terminal stage of a scientific renaissance beginning about the mid-fifteenth century, and characterized chiefly by its full exploration of classical scientific texts, which was aided particularly by the invention of printing; the scientific renaissance was itself regarded as a classical reaction against the gothic barbarity of the Middle Ages. This interpretation is in effect an extension of Bacon's, to which I referred earlier; an extension which Bacon himself was unable to make because he did not know that the revolution he sought was going on around him. Clearly, if such a view is accepted, it attaches a very great importance indeed to the activity of the scholar scientists of the Renaissance who, besides polishing and extending the works of the most authoritative ancient authors, shed a full light on others, such as Lucretius, Celsus, and Archimedes, whose writings had not previously been widely studied.

The merits of this hypothesis of the origin of the scientific revolution are as obvious as its defects. It draws attention to the weight of the contribution of sheer scholarship, and of the amazing Hellenophile instinct of the Renaissance, to the change in science which occurred between 1550 and 1700. No one would deny the connection between the mechanical, corpuscular philosophy of the seventeenth century, and *De natura rerum*; nor the significance for anatomy of the intensive study of Galen; nor would he dispute that the virtual rediscovery of Archimedes transformed geometry, and ultimately algebra. Equally, however, it is clear that this is far from being the whole story: the instances I have quoted are not universally typical ones. The history of mechanics before Galileo, which has been so elaborately worked out in the present half-century, proves the point. Medieval science was not abruptly cut short by a classical revival called a renaissance: it had much – how much must be the subject of continuing research – to contribute to the formation of modern science. Very important threads in the scientific revolution are not really traceable to antiquity at all, at least not through the channels of scholarship; here the chemical sciences furnish examples. Above all, the renaissance-scholarship interpretation fails to account for the *change* in science. If anything is fairly certain, it is that the intention of the Renaissance was the imitation of antiquity, and there is evidence that the ideal extended to the scholar-scientists. Yet the pursuit of this ideal seems to have endured least long in science, of all the learned subjects it had ceased to have force long before the end of the sixteenth century. There never was a true Palladian age in science, and the limitations that had bound the Greeks themselves were relatively soon transcended in Europe. Why this was so is really the whole point at issue, and the Renaissance-scholarship interpretation does not squarely face it.

Nevertheless, if that view is not completely adequate it must serve as an element in any more complete interpretation. The different view of the importance of scholarly activities, this time in the Middle Ages, that I mentioned previously, has won ground much more recently. It is one that the non-medievalist has some difficulty in evaluating, and it would be inappropriate for him to criticize it. I had better state my conception of its tenets at the risk of oversimplification; that medieval philosophers evolved a theory for the investigation of natural phenomena which was essentially that applied with success in the scientific revolution. It is not claimed for those who elaborated this theory that they were themselves as eminent in experiment, or observation, or the use of mathematics as their successors; its applications – other than to optical phenomena and the discussion of impetus – seem to have been few and sporadic. It was a scholar's method of science, vindicated by some successes, which only awaited general application to transform the whole exploration of nature, and this the method found in the late sixteenth and seventeenth centuries. Again, then, great importance is attached to the role of the scholar; the scientific revolution, it might be said, is the direct consequence of a philosophic revolution.

At the same time, it is evident that there is a measure of incompatibility between these two alternative appraisals of the supposed contribution of scholars to the genesis of modern science. One lays emphasis on content, the other on method; if the medieval ideas on method are pre-eminently important, then the Renaissance revival of classical science is irrelevant, and vice versa. One view, if allowed to fill the whole picture, tends to obscure the other. We are not forced to an exclusive choice, however, and I think it may be granted that a compromise which allows room for both views is possible. It would seem to be the case that while one theory best accounts for certain aspects of the development of science in the sixteenth and seventeenth centuries, the other best explains other aspects. Nor should it be forgotten that changes of emphasis within the scope of the classical tradition may be attributable, in part at least, to changed ideas of method derived from the Middle Ages. I mentioned earlier the rediscovery of Lucretius in 1417, and the connection of this with the mechanical philosophy of two and a half centuries later; it may well be that new ideas on the form and structure of a scientific theory had much to do with the preference for the atomistic tradition in Greek thought over the Aristotelian thus evinced. The fuller acquaintance that textual scholarship conferred with those relics of Greek science which best exemplified the newer medieval notions of scientific procedure might have built up a greater pressure for the further application of those notions. For example, if Galileo, unknown to himself, inherited a method of scientific inquiry from medieval philosophers, he thought of himself (on occasion) as practising a method used with success by Archimedes.

The medievalist view, if I may so term it, raises in a peculiarly acute form the question which seems central to my problem. Is the effective and creative impulse, which urged men to abandon not merely the philosophy and doctrines of medieval science but even their Greek foundations, to be found in the dissatisfaction of learned men with established modes of inquiry, and the theories and practices to which they gave rise? In short, was the scientific revolution in the main the product of a sense of intellectual frustration and sterility? If we think this was the case, and that it was the same philosophers, scholars and intellectuals who suffered this frustration, who found a way of breaking through it to a more rewarding kind of inquiry and a more satisfying mode of scientific explanation, then our historical seeking is at an end. We might of course go on to inquire where this frustration originated and what brought it into being, and we might also ask what factors enabled the learned men of science to break through it, but at least we should have established their crucial role in the actual break-through, and all else would be ancillary.

That such frustration was experienced hardly requires demonstration. It is expressed by Vesalius, when he laments – with whatever element of exaggeration and ingratitude – the wasted effort into which too uncritical a confidence in the exactitude of Galen had led him; by Copernicus, when he speaks of the disagreement of mathematicians, and their ineptitude: *'Rem quoque praecipuam, hoc est mundi formam, ac partium eius certam symmetriam non potuerunt invenire, vel ex illis colligere'*; and surely conspicuously enough by Galileo. The latter's is the attitude of one who has broken out of the dead circle of ancient thought, and who can, from reliance on his own new knowledge, pity as well as condemn those still bound by the chains of authority:

> Oh, the inexpressible baseness of abject minds! To make themselves slaves willingly; to accept decrees as inviolable; to place themselves under obligation and to call themselves persuaded and convinced by arguments that are so 'powerful' and 'clearly conclusive' that they themselves cannot tell the purpose for which they were written, or what conclusion they serve to prove! . . . Now what is this but to make an oracle out of a log of wood and run to it for answers; to fear it, revere it, and adore it?

Now what the medievalists contend for is, I take it, that such an attitude to authority was already nascent in the Middle Ages, and that it was not merely negative but creative. I quote Dr Crombie's very plain statement, from the first page of his book on *Grosseteste and Experimental Science* (Oxford, 1953):

> Modern science owes most of its success to the use of these inductive and experimental procedures, constituting what is often called 'the experimental method'. The thesis of this book is that the modern, systematic understanding of at least the qualitative aspects of this method was created by the philosophers of the West in the thirteenth century. It was they who transformed the Greek geometrical method into the experimental science of the modern world.

Why was it necessary to devise new inductive and experimental procedures at all at this point? **Dr Crombie** finds the answer to this question in the problem presented to Western natural philosophers by the scientific texts recently made available to them: 'How is it possible to reach with the greatest possible certainty true premises for demonstrated knowledge of the world of experience, as for example the conclusions of Euclid's theorems are demonstrated?'

This view places the genesis of the scientific revolution at a very high level of intellectual achievement, which is still maintained if we transfer our attention to a somewhat different field from Crombie's, namely the history of theories of mechanics from the Middle Ages down to the time of Galileo. Here again we may note, not merely striking dissatisfaction with the Aristotelian explanation of continued motion founded on the total separation of the moving force from the moved inanimate body as well as with certain other features of mechanics of supposedly Aristotelian formulation, but definite and partially successful steps towards more satisfactory concepts. When we come to the critical point, with Galileo himself, we contemplate an intellectual struggle of the most sublime kind, which Professor Koyré has analysed for us. If the ultimate victory here is not the result of prolonged and arduous cerebration, then it is difficult to see what successes could be attributable to thought and reason in science. Just as the medieval criticism of Aristotle had come from scholars, so also it was in the minds of scholars that the battle between old and new in science had to be fought. I should find it difficult to cite an exponent of the 'new philosophy' who did not visualize its fate in those terms.

There is a point here, however, that deserves fuller consideration, and allows the craftsman to enter on the scene. For while we recognize science as a scholarly activity, and the reform of science as an act of learned men, it may plausibly be asked whether the impulse to reform was spontaneously generated among the learned. Was it perhaps stimulated elsewhere? Some support for this suspicion might seem to spring from the emphasis that has been laid on empiricism, not merely in the scientific revolution itself, but among its philosophical precursors. Thus, to quote Dr Crombie again: 'The outstanding scientific event of the twelfth and thirteenth centuries was the confrontation of the empiricism, long present in the West in the practical arts, with the conception of rational explanation contained in scientific texts recently translated from Greek and Arabic'. It is unnecessary to dwell on the well-known interest of at least a few learned men, during the Middle Ages, in such fruits of empirical invention as the magnetic compass, the grinding of lenses and, above all, the important advances in the chemical and metallurgical arts. Similarly, everyone is familiar with the arguments of the Baconian school: that true command – and therefore real if unwitting knowledge – of natural processes had been won by the arts rather than by sciences, and that the scholar would often become more learned if he would consent to apprentice himself to the craftsman. All this might suggest that the increasingly spectacular achievements of empirical technology arrested the attention of scholarly scientists, enforcing some doubt of the rectitude of their own procedures and, still more, leading them to accept as an ideal of science itself that subjection of the natural environment to human purposes which had formerly seemed to belong only to the arts and crafts.

There are two issues here. One is the fact of technological progress, which some philosophical critics contrasted with the stagnation of science. The other is the reaction of learned men to the state of technology and this is more properly our concern. Technological progress was not simply a feature of the Middle Ages and Renaissance; it occurred in the ancient empires, in the Greek world, under the Roman dominion, and even in the so-called 'Dark Ages'. It would be difficult to think of a long period of complete technical stagnation in European history, though individual arts suffered temporary periods of decline. Some craftsmen at some places seem always to have been making their way forward by trial and error. In short, a philosopher of antiquity had as great an opportunity of appreciating the inventiveness of craftsmen as his successors of the sixteenth and seventeenth centuries, and of drawing the same lessons as were drawn then. Indeed, ancient writers were aware of the importance of the crafts in creating the means of civilized existence, and praised works of ingenuity and dexterity; where they differed from the moderns was in their preservation of the distinction between *understanding* and *doing*. They did not conclude that the progressive success of the crafts set up any model of empiricism for philosophy to emulate. They would not have written, as Francis Bacon did, in the opening lines of the *Novum Organum:* 'Man, as the minister and interpreter of nature, does and understands as much as his observations on the order of nature, either with regard to things or the mind, permit him, and neither knows nor is capable of more. The unassisted hand and understanding left to itself possess but little power . . . Knowledge and human power are synonymous.'

It is the philosopher who has modified his attitude, not the craftsman, and the change is essentially subjective. The success of craft empiricism was nothing new in late medieval and early modern times, and if the philosopher became conscious of its significance for science it was not because such success was more dramatic now than in the past. It was always there to be seen, by those who had eyes to see it, and the change was in the eye of the beholder. It is absurd, for instance, to suppose that the introduction of gunpowder and cannon into warfare was in any serious sense the cause of a revival of interest in dynamics, and especially in the theory of the motion of projectiles, during the sixteenth and early seventeenth century. The ancient torsion artillery provided equally dramatic machines in its day, not to mention the crossbow, mangonel and trebuchet of the Middle Ages. The simplest methods of hurling projectiles – the human arm, the sling, the bow – pose problems of motion no less emphatically than more complex or powerful devices and, as everyone knows, appeal to practical experience of this primitive kind was the basis for the development of the concept of impetus. The earliest 'scientific' writers on explosive artillery, such as Tartaglia, did no more than transfer this concept to the operation of a different device.

Such an example reminds us that it may be naïve to assume that even major technical advances suggested, contemporaneously, such questions worthy of scientific inquiry as would, indeed, immediately spring to our own minds. The scientific examination of the three useful forms of iron – cast iron, wrought iron, and steel – did not begin until the early eighteenth century; the geometrical theory of gear-wheels was initiated about fifty years earlier; the serious study of the chemistry of the ceramics industry was undertaken a little later. I choose deliberately examples of practical science each associated with notable developments in late-medieval craftsmanship: the introduction, respectively, of the effective blast-furnace; of the gear-train in the windmill, watermill, mechanical clock, and other devices; and of fine, brightly pigmented, tin-glazed earthenware. The time-lag in each instance between the establishment of a new craft-skill and the effective appearance of scientific interest in it is of the order of 250 years, and in each of these examples it appears *after* the scientific revolution was well under way. If there is some truth in the view that interest in crafts promoted a change in scientific procedures, it is also true that, at a later date, the very success of the new scientific knowledge and methods opened up the possibility of examining craft procedures systematically, which had not existed before.

It would be a *non sequitur* to argue that, because an important measure of technological progress occurred in the Middle Ages (as we are aware), medieval scholars recognized the fact and appreciated its significance. Clearly in many instances they did not – that is why the history of medieval technology is so difficult to reconstruct. Our literary records of the Middle Ages were in large part compiled by scholars; the paucity in them of technological documentation – concerning not merely the use of tools like the carpenter's brace and lathe, but major industries such as papermaking and iron-working – is very conspicuous. The historian of medieval technology is notably better served by the artist than by the scribe. This could hardly have happened, had more than a very few scholars been impressed by the empiricism which brought in the windmill, the magnetic compass, the mechanical clock, and so on.

In any case, I hesitate to conclude that the behaviour of an empirical scientist – that is, I take it, one who observes and experiments both to discover new information and to confirm his statements and ideas – is derivable by virtually direct imitation from the trial and error, haphazard, and fortuitous progress of the crafts. This seems to me to be the defect of the view that sees the new scientist of the seventeenth century as a sort of hybrid between the older natural philosopher and the craftsman. It is easy enough to say that the philosopher thought much and did little, while the craftsman did much but had no ideas, and to see the scientist as one who both thinks and does. But is such a gross simplification really very helpful in describing or explaining a complex historical transition? Neither Copernicus, nor Vesalius, nor Descartes, to name only three, were more craftsmanlike than Ptolemy, Galen, or Aristotle. Surely scientific empiricism is itself a philosophical artefact, or at least the creation of learned men – here I believe Dr Crombie has a very strong point and it stands in about the same relation to craftsmanship as the theory of evolution does to the practices of pigeon-fanciers. It is a highly sophisticated way of finding out about the world in which we live; on the other hand, the notion that direct immersion in the lore of tradesmen was the essential baptism preceding scientific discovery was one of the sterile by-paths from which the scientists of the seventeenth century fortunately emerged after a short time. Modern studies combine in revealing that the empirical element in the scientific revolution, taking the word in its crudest, least philosophical and most craftsmanlike sense, has been greatly exaggerated; correspondingly we are learning to attach more and more significance to its conceptual and intellectual aspects.

This is not to deny that the processes of artisans constituted an important part of the natural environment. If, by an internal displacement, the attention of the natural philosopher was more closely directed to this, and less to his own consciousness and limited academic horizon, he could learn much of what the world is like. As the Middle Ages verged on the Renaissance, an increasingly rich technological experience offered ample problems for inquiry, and besides, much knowledge of facts and techniques. This, apart from their direct technological importance, was the significance for science of the great works of craft-description and invention by Cellini, Agricola, Biringuccio, Palissy, Ercker, Ramelli and others that appeared in the sixteenth century, for while their own scientific content was slight these authors provided materials and methods for the use of others more philosophically equipped than themselves. Science indeed owes much to technology; but we must remember that the debt was itself created by natural philosophers, and other men of learning.

There is no straightforward answer to any question about the whole nature of the scientific revolution. Here it may again be useful to recall the deep distinction between the academic sciences (astronomy, anatomy, mechanics, medicine) and the non-academic sciences (experimental physics, chemistry, botany and zoology, metallurgy) – the latter group being so described because it had no regular place in university studies. Comparing paradigm cases from the two groups, say, astronomy and chemistry, we note that the former was already highly organized, with an elaborate theoretical structure, in the Middle Ages; it used relatively sophisticated techniques, both instrumental and mathematical; searching criticism of one of its fundamental axioms, that is, the stability of the Earth, occurred in the fourteenth century (and indeed long before), while dissatisfaction with its existing condition was vocal and definite before the end of the fifteenth. A fundamental change in ideas came early – in 1543 – and was followed, not preceded, by great activity in the acquisition of new factual material, which in turn prompted fresh essays in theory. All this was the work of learned men, and there was little possibility of craft-influence; even if the pivotal invention of the telescope were a craft invention, its scientific potentialities were perceived by scholars. Chemistry reveals a very different historical pattern in which almost everything said of astronomy is negated. There was no organized chemical science before a comparatively late stage in the scientific revolution; there was no coherent theory of chemical change and reaction; there was no clearly definable classical and medieval tradition to challenge; the conception of chemistry as a branch of natural philosophy was late in establishing itself, and involved a lengthy fact-gathering stage that preceded the formulation of general theories; and in all these developments the influence of craft-empiricism was strong. It can hardly be doubted that the range of chemical phenomena known to craftsmen about 1550 was much greater than that known to scholars, and that, as Professor C. S. Smith has pointed out, craftsmen had developed both qualitative and quantitative techniques of vital necessity to the growth of chemistry as an exact science.

Sometimes, when one turns from considering the history of such a science as mechanics or astronomy to that of, say, chemistry, or a biological subject, it seems as though the transition is from one discipline to another completely alien to the first. Nor is it enough simply to admit that some sciences developed more slowly than others; the situations are really different, so that Lavoisier's work in chemistry cannot be made strictly analogous, point by point, to that of Newton in celestial mechanics or optics. Hence all generalizations concerning the scientific revolution require qualification when the attempt is made to apply them to a particular science.

Perhaps I may illustrate this in the following way. The contributions of craftsmanship to the development of scientific knowledge in the sixteenth and seventeenth centuries seem to be analysable under five heads:

1. the presentation of striking problems worthy of rational and systematic inquiry;
2. the accumulation of technological information susceptible to scientific study;
3. the exemplification of techniques and apparatus adaptable from the purposes of manufacture to those of scientific research;
4. the realization of the scientific need for instruments and apparatus;
5. the development of topics not embraced in the organization of science proper.

The incidence of these contributions is highly variable among the individual sciences. None are strongly relevant in anatomy, medicine, or indeed any biological science, except that 4 would apply to microscopy. All the sciences demonstrate an increasing dependence on the instrument-maker's craft. Again, 4 is relevant to astronomy, while mechanics draws very slightly upon 1 and 2. Chemistry, on the other hand, exemplifies all these possible contributions, and most forms of applied science – other than mathematical sciences – owe much to the fifth contribution. All we can conclude, therefore, is an obvious truism; that those sciences in whose development empiricism played the greatest part are those in which elements derived from craftsmanship have the most effect. It does not follow, however, that the empirical sciences are those that best exhibit the profundity or the nature of the change in scientific thought and work, nor that the theoretical function of scholars is insignificant even in these sciences. Rather the converse would seem to be true, namely that some of those scientists, like Robert Boyle, who at first sight seem to be highly empirical in their scientific attitude and work, were in fact deeply engaged in the search for general theories and laws. The academic and above all the mathematical sciences were not only those that advanced fastest, but they were already regarded as the models for the structure of other sciences, when these should have reached a sufficiently mature stage. In an ascending scale of sophistication, it was regarded as desirable to render all physical science of the same pattern as mechanics and astronomy, and to interpret all other phenomena in terms of the basic physical laws. The first great step towards the attainment of such an ambition was Newton's *Principia*, a work soon regarded by many as the ultimate manifestation of man's capacity for scientific knowledge. I believe it would be wrong to suppose that the scientists of the late seventeenth century, with such rich examples before them, were content to remain indefinitely at the level of empiricism or sublimated craftsmanship, though indeed in many branches of inquiry it was not yet possible to soar far above it. They were aware that the more abstruse and theoretical sciences, where the contributions of learned men had been greatest, were of a higher type than this.

Perhaps I may now summarize the position I have sought to delineate and justify in the following six propositions, in which it is assumed as an axiom that a science is distinguished by its coherent structure of theory and explanation from a mass of information about the way the world is, however, carefully arranged.

1. The scientific revolution appears primarily as a revolution in theory and explanation, whether we view it in the most general fashion, considering the methods and philosophy of the new

scientists, or whether we consider the critical points of evolution in any single science.

2. There is a tradition of logical (or, more broadly, philosophical) preoccupation with the problem of understanding natural phenomena of which the later stages, from the thirteenth to the seventeenth century, have at the lowest estimate some bearing on the attitudes to this problem of seventeenth-century scientists.

3. Some of the most splendid successes of the scientific revolution sprang from its novel treatment of questions much discussed by medieval scholars.

4. These may be distinguished from the 'contrary instances' of success (or an approximation to it) in handling types of natural phenomena previously ignored by philosophers, though familiar in technological experience.

5. While 'scholars' showed increasing readiness to make use of the information acquired by craftsmen, and their special techniques for criticizing established ideas and exploring phenomena afresh, it is far less clear that craftsmen were apt or equipped to criticize the theories and procedures of science.

6. Though the early exploitation of observation and experiment as methods of scientific inquiry drew heavily on straightforward workshop practice, the initiative for this borrowing seems to be with the scholars rather than craftsmen.

I dislike dichotomies: of two propositions, so often neither *a* nor *b* by itself can be wholly true. The roles of the scholar and the craftsman in the scientific revolution are complementary ones, and if the former holds the prime place in its story, the plot would lack many rich overtones had the latter also not played his part. The scholar's function was active, to transform science; the craftsman's was passive, to provide some of the raw material with which the transformation was to be effected. If science is not constructed from pure empiricism, neither can it be created by pure thought. I do not believe that the scientific revolution was enforced by a necessity for technological progress, but equally in a more backward technological setting it could not have occurred at all. If the genesis of the scientific revolution is in the mind, with its need and capacity for explanation, as I believe, it is also true that the nascent movement would have proved nugatory, had it not occurred in a world which offered the means and incentive for its success.

Critical Problems in the History of Science
pp. 3–22
University of Wisconsin Press 1959

10. The Sociological Roots of Science

E. ZILSEL

Were there many separate cultures in which science has developed and others in which it is lacking, the question about the origin of science would generally be recognized as a sociological one and could be answered by singling out the common traits of the scientific in contrast to the non-scientific cultures. Historical reality, unfortunately, is different, for fully developed science appears once only, namely, in modern Western civilization. It is this fact that obscures our problem. We are only too inclined to consider ourselves and our own civilization as the natural peak of human evolution. From this presumption the belief originates that man simply became more and more intelligent until one day a few great investigators and pioneers appeared and produced science as the last stage of a one-line intellectual ascent. Thus it is not realized that human thinking has developed in many and divergent ways – among which one is the scientific. One forgets how amazing it is that science arose at all and especially in a certain period and under special sociological conditions.

It is not impossible, however, to study the emergence of modern science as a sociological process. Since this emergence took place in the period of early European capitalism, we shall have to review that period from the end of the Middle Ages until 1600. Certain stages of the scientific spirit, however, developed in other cultures too, e.g., in classical antiquity and, to a lesser degree, in some oriental civilizations and in the Arabic culture of the Middle Ages. Moreover, the scientific and half-scientific cultures are not independent of each other. In modern Europe the beginnings of science, particularly, have been greatly influenced by the achievements of ancient mathematicians and astronomers and medieval Arabic physicians. We shall, however, discuss not this influence but the sociological conditions which made it possible.

We can, necessarily, give but a sketchy and greatly simplified analysis of this topic here. All details and much of the evidence must be left to a more extensive exposition at another place.

<h2 style="text-align:center">I</h2>

Human society has not often changed so fundamentally as it did with the transition from feudalism to early capitalism. These changes are generally known. Even in a very brief exposition of the problem, however, we must mention some of them, since they form necessary conditions for the rise of science.

1. The emergence of early capitalism is connected with a change in both the setting and the bearers of culture. In the feudal society of the Middle Ages the castles of knights and rural monasteries were the centres of culture. In early capitalism culture was centred in towns. The spirit of science is worldly and not military. Obviously, therefore, it could not develop among clergymen and knights but only among townspeople.

2. The end of the Middle Ages was a period of rapidly progressing technology and technological inventions. Machines began to be used both in production of goods and in warfare. On the one hand, this set tasks for mechanics and chemistry, and, on the other, it furthered causal thinking, and, in general, weakened magical thinking.

3. In medieval society the individual was bound to the traditions of the group to which he unalterably belonged. In early capitalism economic success depended on the spirit of enterprise of the individual. In early feudalism economic competition was unknown. When it started among the craftsmen and tradesmen of the late medieval towns, their guilds tried to check it. But competition proved stronger than the guilds. It dissolved the organizations and destroyed the collective-mindedness of the Middle Ages. The merchant or craftsman of early capitalism who worked in the same way as his fathers had was outstripped by less conservative competitors. The individualism of the new society is a presupposition of scientific thinking. The scientist, too, relies, in the last resort, only on his own eyes and his own brain and is supposed to make himself independent of belief in authorities. Without criticism there is no science. The critical scientific spirit (which is entirely unknown to all societies without economic competition) is the most powerful explosive human society ever has produced. If the

critical spirit expanded to the whole field of thinking and acting it would lead to anarchism and social disintegration. In ordinary life this is prevented by social instincts and social necessities. In science itself the individualistic tendencies are counterbalanced by scientific co-operation. This, however, will be discussed later.

4. Feudal society was ruled by tradition and custom, whereas early capitalism proceeded rationally. It calculated and measured, introduced book-keeping, and used machines. The rise of economic rationality furthered development of rational scientific methods. The emergence of the quantitative method, which is virtually non-existent in medieval theories, cannot be separated from the counting and calculating spirit of capitalistic economy. The first literary exposition of the technique of double-entry book-keeping is contained in the best textbook on mathematics of the fifteenth century, Luca Pacioli's *Summa de arithmetica* (Venice, 1494); the first application of double-entry book-keeping to the problems of public finances and administration was made in the collected mathematical works of Simon Stevin, the pioneer of scientific mechanics (*Hypomnemata mathematica* [Leyden, 1608]), and a paper of Copernicus on monetary reform (*Monetae cudendae ratio* [composed in 1552]) is among the earliest investigations of coinage. This cannot be mere coincidence.

The development of the most rational of sciences, mathematics, is particularly closely linked with the advance of rationality in technology and economy. The modern sign of mathematical equality was first used in an arithmetical textbook of Recorde that is dedicated to the 'governors and the reste of the Companio of Venturers into Moscovia' with the wish for 'continualle increase of commoditie by their travell' (*The Whetstone of Witte* [London, 1557]). Decimal fractions were first introduced in a mathematical pamphlet of Stevin that begins with the words: 'To all astronomers, surveyors, measurers of tapestry, barrels and other things, to all mintmasters and merchants good luck!' (*De thiende* [Leyden, 1585]). Apart from infusions of Pythagorean and Platonic metaphysics, the mathematical writings of the fifteenth and sixteenth centuries first deal in detail with problems of commercial arithmetic and, second, with the technological needs of military engineers, surveyors, architects, and artisans. The geometrical and arithmetical treatises of Piero de' Franceschi, Luca Pacioli, and Tartaglia in Italy, Recorde and Leonard Digges in England, Dürer and Stifel in Germany, are cases in point. Classical mathematical tradition (Euclid, Archimedes, Apollonius, Diophantus) could be revived in the sixteenth century because the new society had grown to demand calculation and measurement.

Even rationalization of public administration and law had its counterpart in scientific ideas. The loose state of feudalism with its vague traditional law was gradually superseded by absolute monarchies with central sovereignty and rational statute law. This political and juridical change promoted the emergence of the idea that metaphysical processes are governed by rational natural laws established by God. This, however, did not occur before the seventeenth century (Descartes, Huyghens, Boyle).

II

We have mentioned a few general characteristics of early capitalistic society which form necessary conditions for the rise of the scientific spirit. In order to understand this development sociologically, we have to distinguish three strata of intellectual activity in the period from 1300 to 1600: the universities, humanism, and labour.

At the universities theology and scholasticism still predominated. The university scholars were trained to think rationally but exercised the methods of scholastic rationalism, which differ basically from the rational methods of a developed economy. Tradesmen are interested in reckoning; craftsmen and engineers in rational rules of operation, in rational investigation of causes, in rational physical laws. Schoolteachers, on the other hand, take an interest in rational distinction and classifications. The old sentence, *'bene docet qui bene distinguit'*, is as correct as it is sociologically significant. Schoolteaching, by its sociological conditions, produces a specific kind of rationality, which appears in similar forms wherever old priests, entrusted with the task of instructing priest candidates, rationalize vague and contradictory mythological traditions of the past. Brahmans in India, Buddhist theologians in Japan, Arabic and Catholic medieval scholastics conform in their methods to an astonishing degree. Jewish Talmudists proceeded in the same way, though, not being priests by profession, they dealt with ritual and canon law rather than with proper theological questions. This school rationality has developed to a monstrous degree in Brahmanic Sankhya-philosophy (sankhya means 'enumeration').

As a rule the specific scholastic methods are preserved when theologians, in the course of social development, apply themselves to secular subject matters. Thus in Indian literature Brahmans who had

entered the service of princes discussed politics and erotics by meticu-
lously distinguishing and enumerating the various possibilities of political and sexual life (Kautilya, Vatsyayana). In a somewhat analogous
way the medieval scholastics and the European university scholars
before 1600 indulged in subtle distinctions, enumerations, and disputa-
tions. Bound to authorities, they favoured quotation and uttered their
opinions for the most part in the form of commentaries and com-
pilations. After the thirteenth century mundane subject-matters were
treated by scholars, too, and, as an exception, even experience was
referred to by some of them. But when the Schoolmen were at all
concerned with secular events they did not, as a rule, investigate causes
and, never, physical laws. They endeavoured rather to explain the end
and meanings of the phenomena. Obviously, the occult qualities and
Aristotelian substantial forms of scholasticism are but rationalizations
of pre-scientific, magic, and animistic teleology. Thus till the middle of
the sixteenth century the universities were scarcely influenced by the
development of contemporary technology and by humanism. Their
spirit was still substantially medieval. It seems to be a general sociological phenomenon that rigidly organized schools are able to offer
considerable resistance to social changes of the external world.

The first representatives of secular learning appeared in the fourteenth century in Italian cities. They were not scientists but secretaries
and officials of municipalities, princes, and the pope looking up with
envy to the political and cultural achievements of the classical past.
These learned officials who chiefly had to conduct the foreign affairs of
their employers became the fathers of humanism. Their aims derive
from the conditions of their profession. The more erudite and polished
their writings, the more eloquent their speeches, the more prestige
redounded to their employers and the more fame to themselves. They
therefore chiefly strove after perfection of style and accumulation of
classical knowledge. In the following centuries the Italian humanists
lost in large part their official connections. Many became free literati,
dependent on princes, noblemen, and bankers as patrons. Others were
engaged as instructors to the sons of princes, and several got academic
chairs and taught Latin and Greek at universities. Their aims remained
unchanged, and their pride of memory and learning, their passion for
fame, even increased. They acknowledged certain ancient writers as
patterns of style and were bound to these secular authorities almost as
strictly as the theologians were to their religious ones. Though
humanism also proceeded rationally, its methods were as different from

scholastic as from modern scientific rationality. Humanism developed the methods of scientific philology, but neglected causal research and was ignorant of physical laws and quantitative investigation. Altogether it was considerably more interested in words than in things, more in literary forms than in contents. Humanism spread over all parts of western and central Europe. Though the professional conditions and intellectual aims of the humanists outside Italy were somewhat more complex, on the whole their methods were the same.[1]

The university scholars and the humanistic literati of the Renaissance were exceedingly proud of their social rank. Both disdained uneducated people. They avoided the vernacular and wrote and spoke Latin only. Further, they were attached to the upper classes, sharing the social prejudices of the nobility and the rich merchants and bankers and despising manual labour. Both, therefore, adopted the ancient distinction between liberal and mechanical arts: Only professions which do not require manual work were considered by them, their patrons, and their public to be worthy of well-bred men.

The social antithesis of mechanical and liberal arts, of hands and tongue, influenced all intellectual and professional activity in the Renaissance. The university-trained medical doctors contented themselves more or less with commenting on the medical writings of antiquity; the surgeons who did manual work such as operating and dissecting belonged with the barbers and had a social position similar to that of midwives. Literati were much more highly esteemed than were artists. In the fourteenth century the latter were not separated from whitewashers and stone-dressers and, like all craftsmen, were organized in guilds. They gradually became detached from handicraft, until a separation was effected in Italy about the end of the sixteenth

---

[1] It seems to be a rather general sociological phenomenon that, where there are professional public officials, secular learning first appears in the form of humanism. In China also after the dissolution of feudalism in the period of Confucius a group of literati officials developed who were chiefly interested in perfection of style and who acknowledged certain ancient writings as literary models. In the following period admission to civil service was made dependent on examinations regarding literary style and knowledge of antiquity. In China even calligraphy belonged to the formal requirements of higher education, Chinese writing characters being more complicated than European ones. Secular scribes, proud of their profession and learning and bound to ancient models, can be found also in ancient Egypt and the neo-Parthian empire. In classical antiquity there was an abundance of rhetors, grammarians, philologists, and philosophers rather resembling the humanistic literati of the Renaissance. Yet lack of professional civil servants in the republican period prevented development of a perfect correspondence.

century. In the period of Leonardo da Vinci (about 1500) this had not been accomplished. This fact appears rather distinctly in the writings of contemporary artists who over and over again discussed the question as to whether painting and sculpture belong with liberal or mechanical arts. In these discussions the painters usually stressed their relations to learning (painting needs perspective and geometry) in order to gain social esteem. Technological inventors and geographical discoverers, being craftsmen and seamen, were hardly mentioned by the humanistic literati. The great majority of the humanists did not report on them at all. If they mentioned them, they did so in an exceedingly careless and inaccurate way. From the present point of view the culture of the Renaissance owes its most important achievements to the artists, the inventors, and the discoverers. Yet these men entirely recede into the background in the literature of the period.

Beneath both the university scholars and the humanistic literati the artisans, the mariners, shipbuilders, carpenters, foundrymen, and miners worked in silence on the advance of technology and modern society. They had invented the mariner's compass and guns; they constructed paper mills, wire mills, and stamping mills; they created blast furnaces and in the sixteenth century introduced machines into mining. Having outgrown the constraints of guild tradition and being stimulated to inventions by economic competition, they were, no doubt, the real pioneers of empirical observation, experimentation, and causal research. They were uneducated, probably often illiterate, and, perhaps for that reason, today we do not even know their names. Among them were a few groups which needed more knowledge for their work than their colleagues did, and, therefore, got a better education. Among these superior craftsmen the artists are most important. There were no sharp divisions between painters, sculptors, goldsmiths, and architects; but very often the same artist worked in several fields, since, on the whole, division of labour had developed only slightly in the Renaissance. Following from this a remarkable professional group arose during the fifteenth century. The men we have in mind may be called artist-engineers, for not only did they paint pictures, cast statues, and build cathedrals, but they also constructed lifting engines, canals and sluices, guns and fortresses. They invented new pigments, detected the geometrical laws of perspective, and constructed new measuring tools for engineering and gunnery. The first of them is Brunelleschi (1377–1446), the constructor of the cupola of the cathedral of Florence. Among his followers were Ghiberti (1378–

1455), Leone Battista Alberti (1404–72), Leonardo da Vinci (1452–1519), and Vanoccio Biringucci (d. 1538), whose booklet on metallurgy is one of the first chemical treatises free of alchemistic superstition. One of the last of them is Benvenuto Cellini (1500–71), who was a goldsmith and sculptor and also worked as military engineer of Florence. The German painter and engraver Albrecht Dürer, who wrote treatises on descriptive geometry and fortifications (1525 and 1527), belongs to this group. Many of the artist-engineers wrote – in the vernacular and for their colleagues – diaries and papers on their achievements. For the most part these papers circulated as manuscripts only. The artist-engineers got their education as apprentices in the workshops of their masters. Only Alberti had a humanistic education.

The surgeons belonged to a second group of superior artisans. Some Italian surgeons had contacts with artists, resulting from the fact that painting needs anatomical knowledge. The artificers of musical instruments were related to the artist-engineers. Cellini's father, for example, was an instrument-maker, and he himself was appointed as a pope's court musician for a time. In the fifteenth and sixteenth centuries the forerunners of the modern piano were constructed by the representatives of this third group. The makers of nautical and astronomical instruments and of distance meters for surveying and gunnery formed a fourth group. They made compasses and astrolabes, cross-staffs, and quadrants and invented the declinometer and inclinometer in the sixteenth century. Their measuring-instruments are the forerunners of the modern physical apparatus. Some of these men were retired navigators or gunners. The surveyors and the navigators, finally, were also considered as representatives of the mechanical arts. They and the map-makers are more important for the development of measurement and observation than of experimentation.

These superior craftsmen made contacts with learned astronomers, medical doctors, and humanists. They were told by their learned friends of Archimedes, Euclid, and Vitruvius; their inventive spirit, however, originated in their own professional work. The surgeons and some artists dissected, the surveyors and navigators measured, the artist-engineers and instrument-makers were perfectly used to experimentation and measurement, and their quantitative thumb rules are the forerunners of the physical laws of modern science. The occult qualities and substantial forms of the scholastics, the verbosity of the humanists were of no use to them. All these superior artisans had already developed considerable theoretical knowledge in the fields of mechanics, acoustics, chemistry, metallurgy, descriptive geometry, and anatomy. But, since they had not learned how to proceed systematically, their achievements form a collection of isolated discoveries. Leonardo, for example, deals sometimes quite wrongly with mechanical problems which, as his diaries reveal, he himself had solved correctly years before. The superior craftsmen, therefore, cannot be called scientists themselves, but they were the immediate predecessors of science. Of course, they were not regarded as respectable scholars by contemporary public opinion. The two components of scientific method were still separated before 1600 – methodical training of intellect was preserved for upper-class learned people, for university scholars, and for humanists; experimentation and observation were left to more or less plebeian workers.

The separation of liberal and mechanical arts manifested itself clearly in the literature of the period. Before 1550 respectable scholars did not care for the achievements of the nascent new world around them and wrote in Latin. On the other hand, after the end of the fifteenth century, a literature published by 'mechanics' in Spanish, Portuguese, Italian, English, French, Dutch, and German had developed. It included numerous short treatises on navigation, vernacular mathematical text-books, and dialogues dealing with commercial, technological, and gunnery problems (e.g., Étienne de la Roche, Tartaglia, Dürer, Ympyn), and various vernacular booklets on metallurgy, fortification, book-keeping, descriptive geometry, compass-making, etc. In addition there were the unprinted but widely circulated papers of the Italian artist-engineers. These books were diligently read by the colleagues of their authors and by merchants. Many of these books, especially those on navigation, were frequently reprinted, but as a rule they were disregarded by respectable scholars. As long as this separation persisted, as long as scholars did not think of using the disdained methods of manual workers, science in the modern meaning of the word was impossible. About 1550, however, with the advance of technology, a few learned authors began to be interested in the mechanical arts, which had become economically so important, and composed Latin and vernacular works on the geographical discoveries, navigation and cartography, mining and metallurgy, surveying, mechanics, and gunnery. Eventually the social barrier between the two components of the scientific method broke down, and the methods of the superior craftsmen were adopted by academically trained scholars: real science was born. This was achieved about 1600 with William Gilbert (1540–1603), Galileo (1564–1642), and Francis Bacon (1561–1626).

William Gilbert, physician to Queen Elizabeth, published the first printed book composed by an academically trained scholar which was based entirely on laboratory experiment and his own observation (*De magnete* [1600]). Gilbert used and invented physical instruments but neither employed mathematics nor investigated physical laws. Like a modern experimentalist he is critically-minded. Aristotelism, belief in authority, and humanistic verbosity were vehemently attacked by him. His scientific method derives from foundrymen, miners, and navigators with whom he had personal contacts. His experimental devices and many other details were taken over from a vernacular booklet of the compass-maker Robert Norman, a retired mariner (1581).

Galileo's relations to technology, military engineering, and the artist-engineers are often underrated. When he studied medicine at the University of Pisa in the eighties of the sixteenth century, mathematics was not taught there. He studied mathematics privately with Ostilio Ricci, who had been a teacher at the Accademia del Disegno in Florence, a school founded about twenty years earlier for young artists and artist-engineers. Its founder was the painter Vasari. Both the foundation of this school (1562) and the origin of Galileo's mathematical education show how engineering and its methods gradually rose from the workshops of craftsmen and eventually penetrated the field of academic instruction. As a young professor at Padua (1592–1610), Galileo lectured at the university on mathematics and astronomy and privately on mechanics and engineering. At this time he established workrooms in his house, where craftsmen were his assistants. This was the first 'university' laboratory in history. He started his research with studies on pumps, on the regulation of rivers, and on the construction of fortresses. His first printed publication (1606) described a measuring tool for military purposes which he had invented. All his life he liked to visit dockyards and to talk with the workmen. In his chief work of 1638, the *Discorsi*, the setting of the dialogue is the Arsenal of Venice. His greatest achievement – the detection of the law of falling bodies, published in the *Discorsi* – developed from a problem of contemporary gunnery, as he himself declared. The shape of the curve of projection had often been discussed by the gunners of the period. Tartaglia had not been able to answer the question correctly. Galileo, after having dealt with the problem for forty years, found the solution by combining craftsman-like experimentation and measurement with learned mathematical analysis. The different social origin of the two components of his method – which became the method of modern science – is obvious in the *Discorsi*, since he gives the mathematical deductions in Latin and discusses the experiments in Italian. After 1610 Galileo gave up writing Latin treatises and addressed himself to non-scholars. His greatest works, consequently, are written completely or partially in Italian. A few vernacular poets were among his literary favourites. Even his literary taste reveals his predilection for the plain people. His aversion to the spirit and methods of the contemporary professors and humanists is frequently expressed in his treatises and letters.

The same opposition to both humanism and scholasticism can be found in the works of Francis Bacon. No scholar before him had attacked belief in authority and imitation of antiquity so passionately. Bacon was enthusiastic about the great navigators, the inventors, and the craftsmen of his period; their achievements, and only theirs, are set by him as models for scholars. The common belief that it is 'a kind of dishonour to descend to inquiry upon matters mechanical' seems 'childish' to him. Induction, which is proclaimed by him as the new method of science, obviously is the method of just those manual labourers. He died from a cold which he caught when stuffing a chicken with snow. This incident also reveals how much he defied all customs of contemporary scholarship. An experiment of this kind was in his period considered worthy rather of a cook or knacker than of a former lord chancellor of England. Bacon, however, did not make any important discovery in the field of natural science, and his writings abound with humanistic rhetoric, scholastic survivals and scientific mistakes. He is the first writer in the history of mankind, however, to realize fully the basic importance of methodical scientific research for the advancement of human civilization.

Bacon's real contribution to the development of science appears when he is confronted with the humanists. The humanists did not live on the returns from their writings but were dependent economically on bankers, noblemen and princes. There was a kind of symbiosis between them and their patrons. The humanist received his living from his patron and, in return, made his patron famous by his writings. Of course, the more impressive the writings of the humanists, the more famous he became. Individual fame, therefore, was the professional ideal of the humanistic literati. They often called themselves 'dispensers of glory' and quite openly declared fame to be the motive of their own and every intellectual activity. Bacon, on the contrary, was opposed to the ideal of individual glory. He substituted two new aims: 'control of nature' by means of science and 'advancement of learning'. Progress instead of fame means the substitution of a personal ideal by an objective one. In his *Nova Atlantis* Bacon depicted an ideal state in which technological and scientific progress is reached by planned co-operation of scientists, each of whom uses and continues the investigations of his predecessors and fellow-workers. These scientists are the rulers of the New Atlantis. They form a staff of public officials organized in nine groups according to the principle of division of labour. Bacon's ideal of scientific co-operation obviously originated in the ranks of manufacturers and artisans. On the one hand, early capitalistic manual workers were quite accustomed to use the experience of their colleagues and predecessors, as is stressed by Bacon himself and occasionally mentioned by Galileo. On the other hand, division of labour had advanced in contemporary society and in the economy as a whole.

Essential to modern science is the idea that scientists must co-operate in order to bring about the progress of civilization. Neither disputing scholastics nor literati, greedy of glory, are scientists. Bacon's idea is substantially new and occurs neither in antiquity nor in the Renaissance. Somewhat similar ideas were pointed out in the same period by Campanella and, occasionally, by Stevin and Descartes. As is generally known, Bacon's *Nova Atlantis* greatly influenced the foundation of learned societies. In 1654 the Royal Society was founded in London, in 1663 the Académie française in Paris; in 1664 the *Proceedings* of the Royal Society appeared for the first time. Since this period co-operation of scientists in scientific periodicals, societies, institutes, and organizations has steadily advanced.

On the whole, the rise of the methods of the manual workers to the ranks of academically trained scholars at the end of the sixteenth century is the decisive event in the genesis of science. The upper stratum could contribute logical training, learning, and theoretical interest; the lower stratum added causal spirit, experimentation, measurement, quantitative rules of operation, disregard of school authority, and objective co-operation.

III

The indicated explanation of the development of science obviously is incomplete. Money economy and co-existent strata of skilled artisans and secular scholars are frequent phenomena in history. Why, nevertheless, did science not develop more frequently? A comparison with classical antiquity can fill at least one gap in our explanation.

Classical culture produced achievements in literature, art, and philosophy which are in no way inferior to modern ones. It produced outstanding and numerous historiographers, philologists, and grammarians. Ancient rhetoric is superior to its modern counterpart both in refinement and in the number of representatives. Ancient achievements are considerable in the fields of theoretical astronomy and mathematics, limited in the biological field, and poor in the physical sciences. Only three physical laws were correctly known to the ancient scholars: the principles of the lever and of Archimedes and the optical law of reflection. In the field of technology one difference is most striking: machines were used in antiquity in warfare, for juggleries, and for toys but were not employed in the production of goods. On the whole, ancient culture was borne by a rather small upper class living on their rents. Earning money by professional labour was always rather looked down upon in the circles determining ancient public opinion. Manual work was even less appreciated. In the same manner as in the Renaissance, painters and sculptors gradually detached from handicraft and slowly rose to social esteem. Yet their prestige never equalled that of writers and rhetors, and even in the period of Plutarch and Lucianus the greatest sculptors of antiquity would be attacked as manual workers and wage-earners. Compared with poets and philosophers, artists were rarely mentioned in literature, and engineers and technological inventors virtually never. The latter presumably (very little is known of them) were superior artisans or emancipated slaves working as foremen. In antiquity rough manual work was done by slaves.

As far as our problem is concerned, this is the decisive difference between classical and early capitalistic society. Machinery and science cannot develop in a civilization based on slave labour. Slaves generally are unskilled and cannot be entrusted with handling complex devices. Moreover, slave labour seems to be cheap enough to make introduction of machines superfluous. On the other hand, slavery makes the social contempt for manual work so strong that it cannot be overcome by the educated. For this reason ancient intellectual development could not overcome the barrier between tongue and hand. In antiquity only the least prejudiced among the scholars ventured to experiment and to dissect. Very few scholars, such as Hippocrates and his followers,

Democritus and Archimedes, investigated in the manner of modern experimental and causal science, and even Archimedes considered it necessary to apologize for constructing battering-machines. All these facts and correlations have already been pointed out several times.

It may be said that science could fully develop in modern Western civilization because European early capitalism was based on free labour. In early capitalistic society there were very few slaves, and they were not used in production but were luxury gifts in the possession of princes. Evidently lack of slave labour is a necessary but not a sufficient condition for the emergence of science. No doubt further necessary conditions would be found if early capitalistic society were compared with Chinese civilization. In China, slave labour was not predominant, and money economy had existed since about 500 B.C. Also there were in China, on the one hand, highly skilled artisans and, on the other, scholar-officials, approximately corresponding to the European humanists. Yet causal, experimental, and quantitative science not bound to authorities did not arise. Why this did not happen is as little explained as why capitalism did not develop in China.

The rise of science is usually studied by historians who are primarily interested in the temporal succession of the scientific discoveries. Yet the genesis of science can be studied also as a sociological phenomenon. The occupations of the scientific authors and of their predecessors can be ascertained. The sociological function of these occupations and their professional ideals can be analysed. The temporal succession can be interrupted and relevant sociological groups can be compared to analogous groups in other periods and other civilizations – the medieval scholastics with Indian priest-scholars, the Renaissance humanists with Chinese mandarins, the Renaissance artisans and artists with their colleagues in classical antiquity. Since, in the sociology of culture, experiments are not feasible, comparison of analogous phenomena is virtually the only way of finding and verifying causal explanations. It is strange how rarely investigations of this kind are made. As the complex intellectual constructs are usually studied historically only, so sociological research for the most part restricts itself to comparatively elementary phenomena. Yet there is no reason why the most important and interesting intellectual phenomena should not be investigated sociologically and causally.

American Journal of Sociology 1941–2
pp. 544–60

11 The Scientific Revolution and the Protestant Reformation

S. F. MASON

From the inception of the scientific revolution and the Protestant Reformation during the sixteenth century, it has been noted by various authors that there were some similarities between the new science and the new religion, and that Protestant beliefs have been more conducive than the Catholic faith to the promotion of scientific activity. The sixteenth-century medical writer, Richard Bostocke, held the view that the reform of religion had been indispensable to the reform of medicine, and that Copernicus and Paracelsus had restored the sciences just as Luther and Calvin had restored religion. Referring to the new iatro-chemistry, Bostocke wrote, that Paracelsus

> 'was not the author and inventor of this arte as the followers of the Ethnicks physicke doe imagine, . . . no more than Wicklife, Luther, Oecolampadius, Swinglius, Calvin, etc., were the authors and inventors of the Gospell and religion in Christes Church when they restored it to his puritie, according to God's word. . . . And no more than Nicolaus Copernicus, which lived at the time of this Paracelsus, and restored to us the place of the starres according to the trueth . . . is to be called the author and inventor of the motions of the starres.'

During the following century, Thomas Sprat, who was himself an Anglican Churchman and a Fellow of the newly formed Royal Society, noted 'the agreement that is between the present design of the Royal Society, and that of our Church in its beginning. They both may lay equal claim to the word Reformation; the one having compassed it in Religion, the other purposing it in Philosophy'. A little more than a hundred years later, Joseph Priestley, the chemist and Unitarian minister, expressed the view that, in the degree to which the Pope patronized science and polite literature, he 'was cherishing an enemy in disguise', for he had 'reason to tremble even at an air pump, or an electrical machine'. During the nineteenth century, when statistics came into vogue, Alphonse de Candolle, who came of a Huguenot family of scientists, pointed out that of the ninety-two foreign members elected to the Paris Academy of Sciences in the period 1666–1866, some seventy-one had been Protestant in their religion and sixteen had been Catholic, while the remaining five were either indeterminate or Jews. Correlating these figures with the respective religious populations of Europe out-side of France, 107 million Catholics and 68 million Protestants, Candolle showed that more than six times as many Protestants as Catholics had become eminent enough in science to be elected to foreign membership of the Paris Academy of Sciences. Such a correla-tion left out of account the scientists of France, and so Candolle examined the religious affiliations of the foreign members of the Royal Society at two periods, 1829 and 1869, when there were more French scientists included than at other times. He found that at both periods there were about equal numbers of Catholic and Protestant foreign members of the Royal Society, yet outside of the United Kingdom there were 139 million Catholics and 44 million Protestants, figures which substantiated his view that Protestants tended to predominate over Catholics amongst the great scientists of Europe. Subsequent studies of the religious affiliations of scientists, which have been listed by R. K. Merton in his analysis of the connections between Puritanism and science in seventeenth-century England, have confirmed and amplified the general burden of Candolle's findings, and more recent studies have extended the period covered by his correlation to the sixteenth and the twentieth centuries.

The occurrence of a preponderance of Protestants over Catholics among the important scientists of modern Europe may be ascribed to three main factors: first, a concordance between the early Protestant ethos and the scientific attitude; secondly, the use of science for the attainment of the religious aims of the later Calvinists, notably the English Puritans; and thirdly, a certain congruity between the more abstract elements of the Protestant theologies and the theories of modern science. The first factor seems to have been common to both of the main branches of the Reformation and to most of the significant developments composing the scientific revolution. In their early days, both the Swiss and the German Reformers taught that man should reject the guidance and the authority of the priests of the Catholic faith and should seek for spiritual truth in his own religious experience: he should interpret the Scriptures for himself. Similarly the early modern scientists turned away from the systems of the ancient philosophers and the medieval schoolmen to search for scientific truth in their own empirical and theoretical experiences: they interpreted Nature for themselves. Thomas Sprat, who belonged to the Calvinist tradition, well expressed such a consonance of aim between early modern science and Protestantism when he wrote that the Anglican Church and the

Royal Society 'may lay equal claim to the word Reformation; the one having compassed it in Religion, the other purposing it in Philosophy'.

> 'They both have taken a like course to bring this about; each of them passing by the corrupt copies, and referring themselves to the perfect Originals for their instruction; the one to the Scripture, the other to the huge Volume of Creatures. They are both accused unjustly by their enemies of the same crimes, of having forsaken the Ancient Traditions, and ventured on Novelties. They both suppose alike that their Ancestors might err; and yet retain a sufficient reverence for them. They both follow the great Precept of the Apostle of trying all things. Such is the harmony between their interests and tempers.'

Early Lutheranism also seems to have been in accord with the scientific attitude, for the earliest technical study of the new Copernican theory of the world came from two scholars of the University of Wittenberg, which was the centre of the German Reformation, even though Luther himself, like Calvin, was opposed to the Copernican theory on the grounds that it conflicted with the literal word of the Scriptures. Rheticus, professor of mathematics in Wittenberg, studied under Copernicus, and published in 1540 the first printed account of the new heliocentric theory, while his colleague, Reinhold, professor of astronomy in Wittenberg, published in 1551 the first astronomical tables based on the Copernican theory.

The second factor helping to account for the prominence of Protestants among the great scientists of modern Europe, the utilization of science for religious ends, appears to have become important amongst the Calvinists of the seventeenth century, notably the English Puritans, who stressed the religious duty of performing 'good works', and who placed scientific activity amongst the good works beneficial to humanity. Neither Luther nor Calvin had laid much emphasis upon the religious importance of performing good works. Luther had taught that inner faith sufficed for man's salvation, though his outward actions and works should conform to his inner faith. Calvin taught that a certain number of elect persons were predestined to salvation, no one being able to know, however, whether he were saved or not, and that a man should behave as though he were saved even if he felt that he were lost. The later followers of Calvin felt an imperative need to know whether they were saved or whether they were lost, and the original doctrine was modified successively by the Scotch, Dutch, and English Calvinists, so that by the mid-seventeenth century it had become generally accepted by the Puritans that the continuous performance of good works indicated that a man was saved. Among the good works sanctioned by the Puritan ethic were scientific studies. The Puritan divine, John Cotton, writing in 1654, went so far as to declare that the study of Nature was a positive Christian duty.

'To study the nature, and course, and use of all God's works is a duty imposed by God on all sorts of men; from the King that sitteth upon the Throne to the Artificer . . .

Reas. 1. God's glory which is seen in the creatures . . .

Reas. 2. Our own benefit; both of the body for health, as in the knowledge of many medicinall things; and of soule for Instruction, which may be learned from the creatures; and of the estate for gain, when we know the worth and use of each thing.

Use. 1. To reprove the streight-heartednesse of most who study no further the creatures, then for necessity or pastime. The Gentlemen onely observeth so much of the nature of Dogs, and Haukes, and Phesants, and Patridges, etc., as serveth for his game. The Tradesman looketh onely at the nature and use of such things as whereby he getteth his living, whether Sheep, Beasts, Skins, Wool, Spices, Fishes, Foule, etc.

But studying the nature of all things, which by observation and conference men might learn one of another, would enlarge our hearts to God, and our skil to usefulnesse to ourselves and others . . . Yea, Schollers here are not to be excused who study onely some general causes and properties of the creatures, as the principles of naturall bodies, their motion, time, place, measure, etc., but neglect to apply their studies to the nature and use of all things under heaven.'

Such a point of view permeated the consciousness of the men composing the first generation of the Royal Society, among whom the Puritans were prominent. Robert Boyle, who was of this generation, in his last will and testament wished the Fellows of the Royal Society 'a most happy success in their laudable attempts to discover the true nature of the works of God, and praying that they and all other searchers into physical truths may cordially refer their attainments to the glory of the Author of Nature and the benefit of mankind'.

Of the two factors discussed hitherto with regard to the prevalence of Protestants among the important scientists of modern Europe, it was perhaps the second, which was marked among the later Calvinists, that had the greater weight. The anti-authoritarianism and empirical individualism common to the early Protestant and modern scientist gave at best a relation of congruity, while the later Calvinist promotion of good works gave a positive impulse to scientific activity. In this connection it is of interest to note that after the days of Galileo and Kepler the main centres of scientific activity passed from Catholic Italy and Lutheran Germany to lands which had come specifically under the influence of Calvinism: England with her Puritans, Holland with her Calvinist Church, and France with her Huguenots, and her Calvinists within the creed, the Jansenists. After the foundation of the Royal Society of London and the Paris Academy of Sciences in the 1660s, the English and the French remained pre-eminent in the field of science for the next century and a half, and while the Dutch lost ground during the eighteenth century, the earlier homes of Calvinism, Scotland and Switzerland, became notable for their scientists in the same period. In Germany and Italy, however, it was not until the nineteenth century that scientists of the calibre of Galileo and Kepler appeared again.

While Protestant attitudes were in accord with, or were conducive to, the pursuit of scientific activities, neither Protestantism nor modern science consisted alone of a set of rules and values guiding human behaviour. Both developed bodies of theory, and the degree to which Protestant theologies have been congruent with the theories of science is a matter relevant to the problem of the influence of Protestantism upon modern science. Historians of the relations between science and religion, for the most part, have considered that Protestant theologies have had little or no influence, or at worst a discouraging effect, upon the development of science:

> 'The negative bearing of the Reformation on freethought,' wrote J. M. Robertson, 'is made clear by the historic fact that the new currents of thought which broadly mark the beginning of the "modern spirit" arose in its despite, and derive originally from outside its sphere. It is to Italy, where the political and social conditions always tended to frustrate the Inquisition, that we trace the rise alike of modern deism, modern Unitarianism, modern pantheism, modern physics, and the tendency to rational atheism.'

In less trenchant terms, A. D. White expressed a similar opinion, and in a more analytical study of the problem, R. K. Merton was of the view that it is 'to the religious ethos, not the theology, that we must turn if we are to understand the integration of science with religion in seventeenth-century England'.

The impulse which the religious ethos gave to scientific activity was perhaps the most important single element integrating science with religion in seventeenth-century England, but it cannot be said that the men of the time fully separated their natural philosophy from their theology. Moreover the medieval view of the world had been composed of a theology and a natural philosophy which were closely integrated, and its overthrow was accomplished simultaneously, though in a piecemeal fashion, on the one hand by the Protestant Reformers who criticized the theological aspects, and on the other by the scientists who criticized the cosmological features. In the development of the new sciences and the new theologies it is possible to discern that the criticisms of the Calvinists and of the astronomers proceeded along lines which bore some similarity one to the other, and that both prepared the way for a new mechanical-theological world view, which enjoyed considerable popularity during the late seventeenth and eighteenth centuries.

The *leit-motif* of the medieval view of the universe to which both the Protestant Reformers and the early modern scientists took exception was the concept of hierarchy. The concept was rooted in the idea that the universe was made up of a graded chain of beings, stretching down from the Deity in the empyrean Heaven at the periphery of the world, through the hierarchies of angelic beings inhabiting the celestial spheres, to the ranks of mankind, animals, plants, and minerals of the lowly terrestrial sphere at the centre of the cosmic system. In such a view of the world even the material elements were regarded as graded in perfection. In particular the four terrestrial elements were thought to be susceptible naturally only to linear motions, which had a beginning and end like all terrestrial phenomena, whilst the fifth element of the heavenly bodies moved naturally with the eternality and perfection of uniform circular motion. According to the generally received theory of mechanics a body in motion required the constant action of a mover, and an important integration of ancient natural philosophy with early Christian theology had occurred through the identification of the movers of the heavenly bodies with the angelic beings mentioned in the Scriptures. . . .

Annals of Science, 1953
pp. 64–69
[For an able statement of the opposite thesis to Mason's, the reader is referred to L. S. Fener *The Scientific Intellectual*, New York, 1963.]

12 National Styles in Science

P. DUHEM

In every nation we find some men who have the ample type of mind, but there is one people in whom this ampleness of mind is endemic; namely, the English people.

Let us look, in the first place, among the written works produced by the English genius for the two marks of the ample and weak mind: one, an extraordinary facility for imagining very complicated collections of concrete facts; and two, an extreme difficulty in conceiving abstract notions and formulating general principles.

What is it that strikes the French reader when he opens an English novel, a masterpiece of a great novelist like Dickens or George Eliot, or a first attempt by a young authoress aspiring to literary fame? What strikes one is the lengthy, minute character of the descriptions. At first he feels his curiosity piqued by the picturesqueness of each object, but he soon loses sight of the whole. The numerous images that the author has evoked for him flow confusedly into one another, while new images pour in constantly only to increase this disorder; before you are a quarter of the way through the description, you have forgotten the beginning of it, and you turn the pages without reading them, fleeing from this nightmarish series of concrete things. What this deep but narrow sort of French mind wants are the descriptions of a Loti, abstracting and condensing in three lines the essential idea, the soul of a whole landscape. The Englishman has no such requirements. All those visible, palpable, tangible things that the novelist enumerates and describes minutely are seen by his compatriots, without any trouble, as a whole: each thing in its place and with all its characteristic details. The English reader sees a charming picture where we French perceive nothing but a chaos importuning us.

This opposition between the French mind, strong enough to be unafraid of abstraction and generalization but too narrow to imagine anything complex before it is classified in a perfect order, and the ample but weak mind of the English will come home to us constantly while we compare the written monuments raised by these two peoples.

Do we wish to verify this in the works of the dramatists? Take one of Corneille's heroes, Auguste, hesitating between revenge and mercy, or Rodrigue deliberating between his filial piety and his love. Two feelings wage a dispute for his heart; but what a perfect order there is in their discussion! Each takes the floor in turn, like two lawyers before the bar expounding in perfectly finished briefs their reasons why they will win the case, and when the reasons on both sides have been clearly expounded, the will of man puts an end to the debate through a precise decision, resembling a judicial degree or a conclusion in geometry.

And now, opposite the Auguste or Rodrigue of Corneille place the Lady Macbeth or Hamlet of Shakespeare: what a mess of confused, imperfect thoughts, with vague, incoherent outlines, dominating and being dominated at the same time! The French spectator, shaped by our classical theatre, tries in vain to *understand* such characters; that is, to deduce clearly from a definite setting that multitude of attitudes and of inexact and contradictory words. The English spectator does not assume this undertaking; he does not seek to understand these characters, to classify and to arrange their gestures in order; he is content to *see* them in their living complexity.

Will this opposition between the French and English minds be recognized by us when we study the philosophical writings? Let us substitute Descartes and Bacon for Corneille and Shakespeare.

What is the preface with which Descartes opens his work? A *Discours de la Méthode*. What is the method of this strong but narrow mind? It consists in 'conducting one's thoughts in order, by beginning with the simplest objects, easiest to know, in order to rise gradually, step by step, so to speak, to the knowledge of the more composite ones, and even presupposing an order among those objects which do not follow one another naturally'.

And what are these objects 'easiest to know' with which 'it is necessary to begin'? Descartes repeated the answer on several occasions: These objects are the *simplest* objects, and by these words he understood the notions that are most abstract and most stripped of sensible accidents, the most universal principles, the most general judgements concerning existence and thought, the first truths of geometry.

Starting from these ideas, from these principles, the deductive method will unroll its syllogisms whose long chain of links, all tested, will firmly tie the most minute consequences to the foundations of the system. 'These long chains of reasons, all simple and easy, which geometers customarily employ in order to carry through their most difficult demonstrations, had prompted me to suppose that the things which may fall within the province of human knowledge follow one another in the same order, and, provided only that we abstain from accepting any as true which are false and that we always keep the order necessary to deduce them from one another, that there cannot be any so remote as to be inaccessible, or so concealed as to be undiscoverable'.

In the use of such a very precise and rigorous method, what is the only cause of error which Descartes feared? It is omission, for he was aware that he had a narrow geometrical mind and that it was hard for him to keep in his mind a complex whole. With respect to the latter alone did he take precautions by preparing a check or test, proposing 'to make from time to time such complete enumerations and such general reviews that he is sure nothing has been omitted'.

Such is the Cartesian method, exactly applied in the *Principes de Philosophie*, where the strong and restricted mind of the geometer has clearly expounded the mechanism by which it operates.

Let us now open the *Novum Organum*. There is no use in looking for Bacon's method in it, for there is none. The arrangement of his book is based on a childishly simple division. In the *Pars destruens*, he called Aristotle names for having 'corrupted natural philosophy with his dialectic and constructed the world with his categories'. In the *Pars aedificans*, he praised the true philosophy, whose object is not to construct a clear and well-ordered system of truths logically deduced from warranted principles. Its object is quite practical, I should go so far as to say industrial: 'We must see what instructions or directions we may especially desire in order to produce or create in a given body some new property, and explain it in simple terms as clearly as possible.'

'For example, if we wish to give the colour of gold to silver, or a greater weight (in conformity with the laws of matter) or transparency to a non-diaphanous stone, or infrangibility to glass, or vegetation to some non-vegetating body, we say we must see what instructions or directions it would be most desirable to receive.'

Will these instructions teach us to conduct and arrange our experiments in accordance with fixed rules? Will these directions teach us the way to classify our observations? Not in the least. Experiments will be made without any preconceived idea, observations will be made by chance, results will be recorded in crude form, as they happen to present themselves, in tables of 'positive facts', 'negative facts', 'degrees' or 'comparisons', and 'exclusion' or 'rejection', in which a French mind would see only a disordered mass of useless reports.

Bacon agreed, it is true, to establish certain categories of prerogatives or privileged facts, but these categories were not classified by him, nor enumerated. He did not analyse them in order to bring under the same heading those categories which might well be reducible to one another. He listed twenty-seven of them as kinds and left us in the dark as to why he closed the list after the twenty-seventh kind. He did not seek an exact formula which characterizes and defines each of the categories of prerogatives, but was content to masquerade it under a name suggestive of a sensuous image, such as isolated facts, or facts that are labelled migratory, indicative, clandestine, clustered, boundary-line, hostile, negotiated, crucial, divorced, luminiferous, gateway, fluid, etc. It is this chaos that certain people – who have never read Bacon – call the Baconian method in opposition to the Cartesian method. In no work does the ampleness of the English mind show more transparently the weakness that it conceals.

If the mind of Descartes seems to haunt French philosophy, the imaginative faculty of Bacon, with its taste for the concrete and practical, its ignorance and dislike of abstraction and deduction, seems to have passed into the life-blood of English philosophy. 'One by one, Locke, Hume, Bentham, and the two Mills have expounded the philosophy of experience and observation. Utilitarian ethics, inductive logic, associationist psychology, these are the great contributions of English philosophy' to universal thought. All these thinkers proceed not so much by a consecutive line of reasoning as by a piling-up of examples. Instead of linking up syllogisms, they accumulate facts. Darwin and Spencer did not engage their adversaries in the learned fencing of discussion; they crushed them by throwing rocks.

The opposition of the French genius and English genius is observed in every work of the mind. It is likewise noticeable in every manifestation of social life.

What can be more different, for example, than French laws, grouped by codes in which the articles of law are methodically arranged under headings stating clearly defined abstract ideas, and English legislation, a prodigious mass of laws and customs, disparate and often contradictory, juxtaposed since the Magna Carta, one after the other, without any new laws abrogating those that preceded them. English judges do not feel embarrassed by this chaotic state of legislation; they do not boast of a Pothier or a Portalis; they are not bothered by the disorderly state of the texts they have to apply; the need for order is a sign of narrowness of mind which, not being able to embrace a whole all at once, needs a guide that can introduce it to each of the elements of that whole, one after the other, without omission or repetition.

The Englishman is essentially conservative; he keeps every tradition, regardless of its source. He is not shocked to see a relic of Cromwell's time next to one of the era of Charles I; the history of his country appears to him just as it has been: a series of diverse contrasting facts, in which each political party has perchance met with success or failure, and has committed in turn criminal and glorious deeds. Such traditionalism, respectful of the whole past, is incompatible with the strictures of the French mind. The Frenchman wishes to have a clear and simple history which has developed in an orderly and methodic way, a history in which all the events have proceeded strictly from the political principles he boasts of, just as corollaries are deduced from a theorem. And if reality does not furnish him with that history, it will be so much the worse for reality; he will alter the facts, suppress them, invent them, preferring to have to deal with a novel, clear, and methodic history than with a true but confused and complex one.

It is this straitness of mind which makes the Frenchman eager for clarity and method, and it is this love of clarity, order, and method which leads him, in every domain, to throw out or raze to the ground everything bequeathed to him by the past, in order to construct the present on a perfectly co-ordinated plane. Descartes, who was perhaps the most typical representative of the French mind, took it upon himself to formulate (in his *Discourse de la Méthode*) the principles proclaimed by all those who so often have broken the ties of our traditions: 'Thus we see that the buildings undertaken and completed by a single architect are generally more beautiful and better arranged than those which several persons have tried to repair by making use of old walls that had been built for other purposes. So with those old sites which, at first having been only little villages, have become in the course of time big cities, and are usually so badly encompassed, compared with those regular placements that an engineer draws on a plain in his imagination. Although, when we consider each of these buildings by itself, we often find as much or more art in one as in any other, yet, on seeing how they are arranged helter-skelter in all sizes and how they make streets crooked and unequal, one would say that chance, rather than the will of a few men using reason, has thus disposed them.' In this passage the great philosopher praised in advance the vandalism which in the age of Louis XIV was to raze so many monuments of the past; he was a prophet of the Versailles to come.

The Frenchman conceives the development of social and political life only as a perpetual cycle of new beginnings, an indefinite series of revolutions. The Englishman sees in it a continuous evolution. Taine has shown what a dominant influence the 'classical spirit', that is to say, the strong but narrow mind prevalent in most Frenchmen, has had on the history of France. We might just as correctly trace through the course of the history of England the effects of the ample but weak mind of the English people.

Now that we have become acquainted with the diverse manifestations of the power to imagine a multitude of concrete facts accompanied by an inaptitude for abstract ideas, we shall not be astonished to learn that this amplitude and weakness of mind have offered a new type of physical theory – new in contrast to that conceived by the strong but narrow mind – and we shall not be astonished, either, to see this new type attain its highest growth in the works of 'that great English school of mathematical physics whose works are one of the glories of the nineteenth century'.

The Aim and Structure of Physical Theory
pp. 63–69
Princeton University Press 1954

Part Two
SELECT DOCUMENTS

I

The Renaissance

The Renaissance was a many-sided movement to which no brief selection of documents can do justice. The extract from Leonardo's notebooks illustrates his mathematical interest. Albrecht Dürer's mathematical work was still recommended in the seventeenth century. (See p. 127.) In some ways indeed painting was regarded as applied science, particularly where perspective was concerned. Another extract illustrates the revival of Platonism in sixteenth-century Italy, which historians such as Alexander Koyré claim to have been a decisive factor in the rise of mathematics there, before it developed in the rest of Europe. Francis Bacon (p. 121) was as critical of Plato as of Aristotle. He was also deeply contemptuous of Renaissance humanism which, in his view, encouraged young men to concentrate upon the niceties of Ciceronian style at the expense of real problems. Bacon (p. 118) also rejected the teaching of Copernicus who, though Polish by origin, was, educationally speaking, a product of Renaissance Italy. The Aristotelians were equally critical of Plato. Galileo puts this point into the mouth of Simplicio in his dialogue, Two New Sciences.

I Leonardo da Vinci and Mathematics

Leonardo (1452–1519) is often regarded as the archtype of Renaissance scientist, although doubts have been raised about the extent of his originality in this field. He had no connection with the academic world of his time and earned his living by way of architecture and engineering, as well as painting.

From Leonardo's *Notebooks* trans. J. P. Richter.

Mechanics are the paradise of mathematical science, because here we come to the fruits of mathematics.

Every instrument requires to be made by experience.

The man who blames the supreme certainty of mathematics feeds on confusion, and can never silence the contradictions of sophistical sciences which lead to an eternal quackery.

There is no certainty in sciences where one of the mathematical sciences cannot be applied, or which are not in relation with these mathematics.

Anyone who in discussion relies upon authority uses, not his understanding, but rather his memory. Good culture is born of a good disposition; and since the cause is more to be praised than the effect, I will rather praise a good disposition without culture than good culture without the disposition.

Science is the captain, and practice the soldiers.

Of the errors of those who depend on practice without science. Those who fall in love with practice without science are like a sailor who enters a ship without a helm or a compass, and who never can be certain whither he is going.

2 The Platonism of Patrizzi, 1591

Francesco Patrizzi (1529-97), an elder contemporary of Campanella and like him a nature philosopher, studied at Padua. He reacted against its Aristotelian teaching and took up Platonism of which he became an exponent at Ferrara. His Nova Philosophia *was published in 1591. See J. H. Randall* The Career of Philosophy, *1962, pp. 210–11.*

From *Nova Philosophia*

Our mind fixes its attention on those finite spaces, which are suited to be the spaces of earthly bodies. The mind does not separate them from those bodies by abstraction, as some maintain, since these spaces are not at first and in themselves in earthly bodies, but are in fact before all bodies in first space. . . . But the mind by its own force cuts off those parts from that first space, which will be of future use to contemplation or action . . . And since space is the first of all natural things, it is obvious that the science of space, both of the continuous and the discrete, exists before all matter. From the same reason it follows, that mathematics is prior to physics. It is also a mean between the completely incorporeal and the completely corporeal, not for the reason the ancients held, that something incorporeal is formed by abstraction from natural things, but because indeed space is an incorporeal body and a corporeal non-body . . . Hence it is obvious that for the student of nature the science of space is to be studied and taught before natural science . . . Rightly therefore was there set forth at the door of the school of the divine Plato: Let no one ignorant of geometry enter here.

3 Bacon's Criticisms of Renaissance Humanism, 1605

Francis Bacon (1561–1626) was Lord Chancellor of England from 1618 to 1621. His ambition lay in the intellectual rather than the legal sphere and he wrote voluminously about the state of knowledge in his own day. His most famous works are The Advancement of Learning (1605) *and a more ambitious treatise.* The New Organon (1620), *a title which indicates a wish to be regarded as a second and greater Aristotle.*

From *The Advancement of Learning*

There be therefore chiefly three vanities in studies, whereby learning hath been most traduced. For those things we do esteem vain, which are either false or frivolous, those which either have no truth or no use: and those persons we esteem vain, which are either credulous or curious; and curiosity is either in matter or words: so that in reason as well as in experience, there fall out to be these three distempers (as I may term them) of learning; the first, fantastical learning; the second, contentious learning; and the last, delicate learning; vain imaginations, vain altercations, and vain affectations; and with the last I will begin. Martin Luther, conducted (no doubt) by a higher Providence, but in discourse of reason finding what a province he had undertaken against the Bishop of Rome and the degenerate traditions of the church, and finding his own solitude, being no ways aided by the opinions of his own time, was enforced to awake all antiquity, and to call former times to his succors to make a party against the present time; so that the ancient authors, both in divinity and in humanity, which had long time slept in libraries, began generally to be read and revolved . . .

. . . So that these four causes concurring, the admiration of ancient authors, the hate of the schoolmen, the exact study of languages, and the efficacy of preaching, did bring in an affectionate study of eloquence and copie of speech, which then began to flourish. This grew speedily to an excess; for men began to hunt more after words than matter; and more after the choiceness of the phrase, and the round and clean composition of the sentence and the sweet falling of the clauses, and the varying and illustration of their works with tropes and figures, than after the weight of the matter, worth of subject, soundness of argument, life of invention, or depth of judgement. Then grew the flowing and watery vein of Osorius, the Portugal bishop, to be in price. Then did Sturmius spend such infinite and curious pains upon Cicero the orator and Hermogenes the rhetorician, besides his own books of periods and imitation and the like. Then did Car of Cambridge, and Ascham, with their lectures and writings almost deify Cicero and Demosthenes, and allure all young men that were studious unto that delicate and polished kind of learning. Then did Erasmus take occasion to make the scoffing echo; *Decem annos consumpsi in legendo Cicerone* (I have spent ten years in reading Cicero): and the echo answered in Greek, *one, Asine*. Then grew the learning of the schoolmen to be utterly despised as barbarous. In sum the whole inclination and bent of those times was rather towards copie than weight. Here therefore is the first distemper of learning, when men study words and not matter. . . .

4 Bacon's Rejection of Copernicus, 1622

From *De Augmentis Scientiarum*

For long ago have those doctrines been exploded of the Force of the First Mover and the Solidity of the Heaven – the stars being supposed to be fixed in their orbs like nails in a roof. And with no better reason is it affirmed, that there are different poles of the zodiac and of the world; that there is a Second Mover of counter-action to the force of the first; that all the heavenly bodies move in perfect circles; that there are eccentrics and epicycles whereby the constancy of motions in perfect circles is preserved: that the moon works no change or violence in the regions above it; and the like. And it is the absurdity of these opinions that has driven men to the diurnal motion of the earth; which I am convinced is most false. But there is scarce anyone who has made inquiries into the physical causes, as well of the substance of the heavens both stellar and interstellar, as of the relative velocity and slowness of the heavenly bodies; of the different velocity of motion in the same planet; of the course of motions from east to west, and contrary; of their progressions, stationary positions, and retrogressions; of the elevation and fall of the motions in apogee and perigee; of the obliquity of motions, either by spirals winding and unwinding towards the Tropics, or by those curves which they call *Dragons*; of the poles of rotation, why they are fixed in such part of the heaven rather than in any other; and of some plant being fixed at a certain distance from the sun: such an inquiry as this (I say) has hardly been attempted; but all the labour is spent in mathematical observations and demonstrations. Such demonstrations however only show how all these things may be ingeniously made out and disentangled, not how they may truly subsist in nature; and indicate the apparent motions only, and a system of machinery arbitrarily devised and arranged to produce them – not the very causes and truth of things.

5 Alleged Aristotelian Criticisms of the Mathematical Approach, 1632

Galileo Galilei (1564–1642) was professor of mathematics at Pisa and later at Padua. From 1610 he worked mainly in Florence under the patronage of the Grand Duke of Tuscany. In 1616 and again in 1632 he came into conflict with the ecclesiastical authorities over his advocacy of Copernicus. This led to his trial by the Inquisition and the condemnation of his book Two World Systems, *from which this extract is taken.*

From Galileo, *Two World Systems*

Salviati: I do not think that Simplicio is one of these Peripateticks that dissuade their disciples from studying the mathematics, as sciences that vitiate the reason and render it less apt for contemplation.
Simplicio: I would not do so much wrong to Plato, but yet I may truly say with Aristotle that he too much lost himself in, and too much doted upon that his Geometry: for that in conclusion these mathematical subtilties, Salviati, are true in abstract, but applied to sensible and

physical matter they hold not good. For the mathematicians will very well demonstrate for example that a sphere touches a plane in a point, a position like to that in dispute; but when one cometh to the matter, things succeed in quite another way. And so I may say of these angles of contact, and these proportions, which all evaporate into air, when they are applied to things material and sensible.

II

The Role of Experiment

These passages offer contrasting views about the object of making experiments. Bacon believed that numerous experiments should be undertaken in order to draw individual conclusions from each.

These are, one may say, experiments 'in the dark'. Galileo, on the other hand, provides an example of a controlled experiment which leads the observer to draw a general conclusion. Both types of experimental approach were to be found in scientific circles throughout the seventeenth century, as the records of the Royal Society demonstrate. The Baconian approach flourished chiefly among the chemists, the Galilean among the mathematically-minded physicists. Only in the eighteenth century was there a successful mathematical breakthrough in the field of chemistry. It may be argued that Bacon's approach was much more traditional than Galileo's, though to prove this point would need a good deal more evidence. The existence of these two points of view may also suggest that belief in experiment is not enough by itself to create a 'modern' attitude.

6 The Baconian Belief in Experiment, (1) 1605

From *The Advancement of Learning*

Historia Mechanica

For History of Nature Wrought or Mechanical, I find some collections made of agriculture, and likewise of manual arts; but commonly with rejection of experiments familiar and vulgar. For it is esteemed a kind of dishonour unto learning to descend to inquiry or meditation upon matters mechanical, except they be such as may be thought secrets, rarities and special subtilties; which humour of vain and supercilious arrogancy is justly derided in Plato; where he brings in Hippias, a vaunting sophist, disputing with Socrates, a true and unfeigned inquisitor of truth; where the subject being touching beauty, Socrates, after his wandering manner of inductions, put first an example of a fair virgin, and then a fair horse, and then of a fair pot well glazed, whereat Hippias was offended, and said, *More than for courtesy's sake, he did think much to dispute with any that did allege such base and sordid instances:* whereunto Socrates answereth, *You have reason, and it becomes you well, being a man so trim in your vestiments,* etc., and goeth on in an irony. But the truth is, they be not the highest instances that give the securest information; as may be well expressed in the tale so common of the philosopher, that while he gazed upwards to the stars fell into the water; for if he had looked down he might have seen the stars in the water, but looking aloft he could not see the water in the stars. So it cometh often to pass that mean and small things discover great better than great can discover the small; and therefore Aristotle noteth well, *that the nature of every thing is best seen in his smallest portions,* and for that cause he inquireth the nature of a commonwealth, first in a family, and the simple conjugations of man and wife, parent and child, master and servant, which are in every cottage: even so likewise the nature of this great city of the world and the policy thereof must be first sought in mean concordances and small portions. So we see how that secret of nature, of the turning of iron touched with the loadstone towards the north, was found in needles of iron, not in bars of iron.

But if my judgement be of any weight, the use of History Mechanical is of all others the most radical and fundamental towards natural philosophy; such natural philosophy as shall not vanish in the fume of subtile, sublime, or delectable speculation, but such as shall be operative to the endowment and benefit of man's life; for it will not only minister and suggest for the present many ingenious practices in all trades, by a connexion and transferring of the observations of one art to the use of another, when the experiences of several mysteries shall fall under the consideration of one man's mind; but further it will give a more true and real illumination concerning causes and axioms than is hitherto attained.

(11) 1620

From *The New Organon*

Now experiments of this kind have one admirable property and condition; they never miss or fail. For since they are applied, not for the purpose of producing any particular effect, but only of discovering the natural cause of some effect, they answer the end equally well whichever way they turn out; for they settle the question.

But not only is a greater abundance of experiments to be sought for and procured, and that too of a different kind from those hitherto tried; an entirely different method, order, and process for carrying on and advancing experience must also be introduced. For experience, when it wanders in its own track, is, as I have already remarked, mere groping in the dark, and confounds men rather than instructs them. But when it shall proceed in accordance with a fixed law, in regular order, and without interruption, then may better things be hoped of knowledge. . . .

Moreover, since there is so great a number and army of particulars, and that army so scattered and dispersed as to distract and confound the understanding, little is to be hoped for from the skirmishings and slight attacks and desultory movements of the intellect, unless all the particulars which pertain to the subject of inquiry shall, by means of Tables of Discovery, apt, well arranged, and as it were animate, be drawn up and marshalled; and the mind be set to work upon the helps duly prepared and digested which these tables supply.

7 Galileo's Conception of Controlled Experiment, 1623

From *The Assayer* trans Stillman Drake

What Sarsi may have heard – but, from what I see, did not understand very well – was a certain experiment which I exhibited to some gentlemen there at Rome, and perhaps at the very house of Your Excellency, in partial explanation and partial refutation of the 'third motion' attributed by Copernicus to the earth. This extra rotation, opposite in direction to all other celestial motions, appeared to many a most improbable thing, and one that upset the whole Copernican system . . . I used to remove the difficulty by showing that such a phenomenon was far from improbable, and indeed would be in accordance with Nature and practically forced to occur. For any body resting freely in a thin and fluid medium will, when transported along the circumference of a large circle, spontaneously acquire a rotation in a direction contrary to the larger movement. The phenomenon was seen by taking in one's hands a bowl of water and placing in it a floating ball. Then turning about on the toe with this hand extended, one sees the ball turn on its axis in the opposite direction, and complete this revolution in the same time as one's own. In this way the wonder was removed, and in place of it one would be astonished if the earth were not to acquire a contrary rotation when assumed to be a body suspended in a fluid medium and going around a large circle in a period of one year. What I said was designed to remove a difficulty attributed to the Copernican system, and I later added that anyone who would reflect upon the matter more carefully would see that Copernicus had spoken falsely when he attributed his 'third motion' to the earth, since this would not be a motion at all, but a kind of rest. It is certainly true that to the person holding the bowl such a ball appears to move with respect to himself and to the bowl, and to turn upon its axis. But with respect to the wall (or any other external thing) the ball does not turn at all, and does not change its tilt, and any point upon it will continue to point towards the same distant object.

That is what I asserted, and you see it is very different from what Sarsi relates. This experiment, and perhaps others, may have induced someone who was present at our discussion to attribute to me what Sarsi mentions next – that is, a certain natural talent of mine for explaining by means of simple and obvious things others which are more difficult and abstruse. He does not deny me praise for this, but I think this comes from courtesy rather than from his true feelings, for so far as I can see he is not easily persuaded of any talent on my part.

[See also *Newton's experiment* p. 142].

III

The Mathematical Revolution

In the twelfth century, the rediscovery of Aristotelian logic led to the application of logical methods to many branches of learning, especially in theology and canon law. This amounted to a logical revolution. An analogous mathematical revolution took place in the seventeenth century. Galileo's successful application of mathematical methods in dynamics led him to believe that the world was mathematical in its basic structure. Bacon, in contrast, thought that mathematics explained appearances only and not the real world. Galileo himself thought that Aristotelianism was anti-mathematical at heart (p. 119), a view which Randall among others has criticized.

In the educational sphere, mathematics came to be regarded as increasingly important (p. 127). In philosophy, Descartes's application of mathematics was very popular but did not achieve universal acceptance (p. 129). Locke claimed that ethics had the same character as mathematics, but like Bacon he was sceptical about the possibility of reaching true knowledge of the real world by this route.

8 Galileo and the Mathematical Universe, 1623

From *The Assayer* trans Stillman Drake

In Sarsi I seem to discern the firm belief that in philosophizing one must support oneself upon the opinion of some celebrated author, as if our minds ought to remain completely sterile and barren unless wedded to the reasoning of some other person. Possibly he thinks that philosophy is a book of fiction by some writer, like the *Iliad* or *Orlando Furioso*, productions in which the least important thing is whether what is written there is true. Well, Sarsi, that is not how matters stand. Philosophy is written in this grand book, the universe, which stands continually open to our gaze. But the book cannot be understood unless one first learns to comprehend the language and read the letters in which it is composed. It is written in the language of mathematics, and its characters are triangles, circles, and other geometric figures without which it is humanly impossible to understand a single word of it; without these, one wanders about in a dark labyrinth.

Sarsi seems to think that our intellect should be enslaved to that of some other man. . . . But even on that assumption, I do not see why he selects Tycho. . . . Tycho could not extricate himself from his own explanation of diversity in the apparent motion of his comet; but now Sarsi expects my mind to be satisfied and set at rest by a little poetic flower that is not followed by any fruit at all. It is this that Guiducci rejected when he quite rightly said that nature takes no delight in poetry. That is a very true statement; even though Sarsi appears to disbelieve it and acts as if acquainted with neither nature nor poetry. He seems not to know that fables and fictions are in a way essential to poetry, which could not exist without them, while any sort of falsehood is so abhorrent to nature that it is as absent there as darkness is in light.

9 The Value of Mathematics to a Gentleman, 1622

Henry Peacham (1576?–1643?) was a schoolmaster and tutor with an amateur's interest in a wide range of artistic activities including music and painting. His best-known work was The Compleat Gentleman *which was one of many books written during the sixteenth and seventeenth centuries dealing with the education of a gentleman's son. Earlier examples of this kind of thing were Castiglione's* The Courtier *and Elyot's* The Governor, *and as a genre it flourished. Milton's* Of Education *may be regarded as a later example (1644) and Locke's* Education *also (1693).*

From *The Compleat Gentleman*

But in brief, the use you shall have of Geometry will be in surveying your lands, affording your opinion in building anew or translating, making your mills as well for the grinding of corn as throwing forth water from your lower grounds, bringing water far off for sundry uses . . . so that I cannot see how a gentleman, especially a soldier and a commander, may be accomplished without geometry . . . The Authors I would commend unto you for entrance hereunto are in English: Cookes *Principles*, and *The Elements of Geometry* written in Latin by P. Ramus and translated by Mr. Dr. Hood, sometime mathematical lecturer in London; Master Blundeville; Euclid translated into English. In Latin you may have the learned Jesuit Clavius, Melanchthon, Frisius, Valtanus his Geometry Military. Albert Düerer hath written excellently hereof in High Dutch and in French Forcadel upon Euclid with sundry others.

10 Newton's View of Mathematics, 1694

Sir Isaac Newton (1642–1727) is best known for his Principia, *published in 1687. He was a man of immense influence both during his own lifetime and afterwards, and his views on mathematics were not lightly to be disregarded. He was professor at Cambridge from 1669 but in 1696 moved to the Mint of which he became master in 1699. From 1703 until the end of his life he was elected president of the Royal Society.*

From his *Correspondence*, ed. G. H. Turnbull, iii, 359–60

For without the learning in this Article [i.e. theory], a Man cannot be an able and Judicious Mechanick, & yet the contrivance & managemt of Ships is almost wholly Mechanical. Tis true that by good natural parts some men have a much better knack at Mechanical things then others, and on that account are sometimes reputed good Mechanicks, but yet wthout the learning of this Article, they are soe Farr from being soe, as a Man of a good Geometrical head who never learnt the Principles of Geometry, is from being a good Geometer. For whilst Mechanicks consist in the Doctrine of force and motion, and Geometry in that of magnitude and figure; he that can't reason about force and motion, is far from being a true Mechanick, as he that can't reason about magnitude and figure from being a Geometer. A Vulgar Mechanick can practice what he has been taught or seen done, but if he is in an error he knows not how to find it out and correct it, and if you put him out of his road, he is at a stand; Whereas he that is able to reason numbly and judiciously about figure, force and motion, is never at rest till he gets over every rub. Experience is necessary, but yet there is the same difference between a mere practical Mechanick and a rational one, as between a mere practical Surveyor or Guager and a good Geometer, or between an Empirick in Physick and a learned and a rational physitian. Let it be therefore onely considered how Mechanical the frame of a Ship is, and on what a multitude of forces and motions the whole business and managemt of it depends, And then let it be further considered whether it be most for the advantage of Sea affaires that the ablest of our Marriners should be but mere Empiricks in Navigation, or that they should be alsoe able to reason well about those figures, forces, and motions they are hourly concerned in. And the same may be said in a great measure of divers others Mechanical employments, as buildings of Ships, Architecture, Fortification, Engineering.

11 Descartes's Philosophical Method, 1637

René Descartes (1596–1650) was largely responsible for the immense esteem in which mathematical method was held during the seventeenth century. He held no university appointment during his life and perhaps for this reason expressed his views with great freedom and in an attractive literary form. His emphasis upon deductive reasoning perhaps led inevitably to a clash with those Englishmen who were empirically-minded.

From *Discourse on Method*

The long chains of simple and easy reasonings by means of which geometers are accustomed to reach the conclusions of their most difficult demonstrations, had led me to imagine that all things, to the knowledge of which man is competent, are mutually connected in the same way, and that there is nothing so far removed from us as to be beyond our reach, or so hidden that we cannot discover it, provided only we abstain from accepting the false for the true, and always preserve in our thoughts the order necessary for the deduction of one truth from another. And I had little difficulty in determining the objects with which it was necessary to commence, for I was already persuaded that it must be with the simplest and easiest to know, and considering that of all those who have hitherto sought truth in the Sciences, the mathematicians alone have been able to find any demonstrations, that is, any certain and evident reasons, I did not doubt but that such must have been the rule of their investigations. I resolved to commence, therefore, with the examination of the simplest objects, not anticipating, however, from this any other advantage than that to be found in accustoming my mind to the love and nourishment of truth, and to a distaste for all such reasonings as were unsound. But I had no intention on that account of attempting to master all the particular Sciences commonly denominated Mathematics.

12 Descartes's Rejection of Experiment

From John Aubrey, *Brief Lives*

He was so eminently learned that all learned men made visits to him, and many of them would desire him to shew them his Instruments (in those dayes mathematicall learning lay much in the knowledge of Instruments, and, as Sir Henry Savile sayd, in doeing of tricks) he would drawe out a little Drawer under his Table, and shew them a paire of Compasses with one of the Legges broken; and then, for his Ruler, he used a sheet of paper folded double.

Mr Hobbes was wont to say that had Des Cartes kept himselfe wholy to Geometrie that he had been the best Geometer in the world but that his head did not lye for Philosophy. He did very much admire him, but sayd that he could not pardon him for writing in the Defence of Transubstantiation, which he knew to bee absolutely against his judgement, and donne meerly to putt a compliment on the Jesuites.

13 Sprat's Criticisms of Descartes

Thomas Sprat (1635–1713), bishop of Rochester, was, like many other ecclesiastics at this time, closely associated with scientists. In 1667 he published a History of the Royal Society *which explained to the lay reader what was being done. It retains its interest as an historical document.*

From *History of the Royal Society*

Towards the first of these ends, it has been their usual course, when they themselves appointed the Trial, to propose one week, some particular Experiments, to be prosecuted the next; and to debate before-hand, concerning all things that might conduce to the better carrying them on. In this Preliminary Collection, it has been the custom for any of the Society, to urge what came into their thoughts, or memories concerning them; either from the observations of others, or from Books, or from their own Experience, or even from common Fame itself. And in performing this, they did not exercise any great rigour of choosing, and distinguishing between Truths and Falshoods: but a mass altogether as they came; the certain Works, the Opinions, the Ghesses, the Inventions, with their different Degrees and Accidents, the Probabilities, the Problems, the general Conceptions, the miracu-lous Stories, the ordinary Productions, the changes incident to the same Matter in several places, the Hindrances, the Benefits, of Airs, or Seasons, or Instruments: and whatever they found to have been begun, to have fail'd, to have succeeded, in the Matter which was then under their Disquisition.

This is a most necessary preparation, to any that resolve to make a perfect search. For they cannot but go blindly, and lamely, and confusedly about the business, unless they have first laid before them a full Account of it. I confess the excellent Monsieur des Cartes recommends to us another way in his Philosophical Method; where he gives this Relation of his own progress; that after he had run through the usual Studies of youth, and spent his first years in an active life; when he retir'd to search into Truth, he at once rejected all the Impres-sions, which he had before receiv'd from what he had heard, and read; and wholly gave himself over to a reflexion on the naked Ideas of his own mind. This he profess'd to do, that he might lay aside all his old imaginations, and begin anew to write on a white and unblotted soul. This perhaps, is more allowable in matters of Contemplation, and in a Gentleman, whose chief aim was his own delight; and so it was in his own choice, whether or no, he would go farther to seek it, than his own mind: But it can by no means stand with a practical and universal Inquiry. It is impossible, but they, who will only transcribe their own thoughts, and disdain to measure or strengthen them by the assistance of others, should be in most of their apprehensions too narrow, and obscure; by setting down things for general, which are only peculiar to themselves. It cannot be avoided, but they will commit many gross mistakes; and bestow much useless pains, by making themselves wilfully ignorant of what is already known, and what conceal'd.

14 The Influence of Mathematics on John Locke, 1690

John Locke (1632–1704) though perhaps best known as a political philosopher was intensely interested in the science of his day and gave much thought to its implications. He was a member of the Royal Society from 1668.

From *Essay of Human Understanding*

They that are ignorant of *algebra* cannot imagine the wonders in this kind that are to be done by it; and what further improvements and helps, advantageous to other parts of knowledge, the sagacious mind of man may yet find out, it is not easy to determine. This at least I believe: that the *ideas* of quantity are not those alone that are capable of demonstration and knowledge; and that other and perhaps more useful parts of contemplation would afford us certainty, if vices, passions, and domineering interest did not oppose or menace such endeavours.

The *idea* of a supreme Being, infinite in power, goodness, and wisdom, whose workmanship we are and on whom we depend, and the *idea* of ourselves as understanding rational beings, being such as are clear in us, would, I suppose, if duly considered and pursued, afford such foundations of our duty and rules of action as might place *morality amongst the sciences capable of demonstration*: wherein I doubt not but from self-evident propositions, by necessary consequences as incontestable as those in mathematics, the measures of right and wrong might be made out to anyone that will apply himself with the same indifferency and attention to the one as he does to the other of these sciences. The *relation* of other *modes* may certainly be perceived, as well as those of number and extension; and I cannot see why they should not also be capable of demonstration, if due methods were thought on to examine or pursue their agreement or disagreement. *Where there is no property there is no injustice* is a proposition as certain as any demonstration in *Euclid*: for the *idea* of *property* being a right to anything, and the idea to which the name *injustice* is given being the invasion or violation of that right, it is evident that, these *ideas* being thus established, and these names annexed to them, I can as certainly know this proposition to be true as that a triangle has three angles equal to two right ones. Again, *no government allows absolute liberty:* the *idea* of government being the establishment of society upon certain rules or laws which require conformity to them, and the *idea* of absolute liberty being for anyone to do whatever he pleases, I am as capable of being certain of the truth of this proposition as of any in mathematics.

[*But note his scepticism about science:*

And therefore I am apt to doubt that, how far soever human industry may advance useful and *experimental* philosophy *in physical things, scientifical* will still be out of our reach: because we want perfect and adequate *ideas* of those very bodies which are nearest to us and most under our command.]

IV
The Medieval Inheritance

The medieval contribution to science is frequently misunderstood. If we turn to a typical theologian of the thirteenth century, we do not find, nor should we expect to find, examples of early scientific method, save in the sense of logical argument. It is a different story with the logicians of Paris, Oxford and elsewhere in the fourteenth century. Many of these were concerned with problems which Galileo would have recognized as similar to those with which he was concerned. The term 'medieval scholastic' is applied to Aquinas (p. 133) and to the Merton school (p. 136) only at the risk of confusing kinds of intellectual activity which were radically different. It is worth noting that the logicians who are highly regarded in the context of the history of science were denounced by Erasmus and the Renaissance humanists for their alleged logic chopping. Bacon with his non-mathematical legal mind was equally critical. It may well be the case that these logicians in another age would have been fully fledged mathematicians.

15 Thirteenth-century Use of Logic

Thomas Aquinas (1226–74), along with Dun Scotus and William of Ockham, was the greatest of those medieval philosophers who attempted to reconcile Aristotelianism with Christianity. Born in Southern Italy, he moved to Northern Europe where scholasticism, i.e. the application of Aristotelian logic to Christian revelation, was beginning to get under way. He taught at Paris from 1252–58.

From *Summa Theologica* Part 1, question 68

WHETHER THERE ARE WATERS ABOVE THE FIRMAMENT?

We proceed thus to the Second Article:
Objection 1. It would seem that there are not waters above the firmament. For water is by nature heavy, and heavy things tend naturally

downwards, not upwards. Therefore, since the firmament is a sphere, there cannot be water above it.

Objection 2. Further, water is fluid by nature, and fluids cannot rest on a sphere, as experience shows. Therefore, since the firmament is a sphere, there cannot be water above it.

Objection 3. Further, water is an element, and ordered to the generation of composite bodies, according to the relation in which imperfect things stand towards perfect. But bodies of composite nature have their place upon the earth, and not above the firmament, so that water would be useless there. But none of God's works are useless. Therefore there are not waters above the firmament.

On the contrary, It is written (Gen. i. 7): (*God*) *divided the waters that were under the firmament from those that were above the firmament.*

I answer with Augustine that, *These words of Scripture have more authority than the most exalted human intellect. Hence, whatever these waters are, and whatever their mode of existence, we cannot for a moment doubt that they are there.* As to the nature of these waters, all are not agreed. Origen says that the waters that are above the firmament are *spiritual substances.* Therefore, it is written (Ps. cxlviii, 4): *let the waters that are above the heavens, bless the Lord.* To this Basil answers that these words do not mean that these waters are rational creatures, but that *the thoughtful contemplation of them by those who understand fulfills the glory of the Creator.* Hence in the same context, fire, hail, and other like creatures, are invoked in the same way, though no one would attribute reason to these.

We must hold, then, these waters to be material, but their exact nature will be differently defined according as opinions on the firmament differ. For if by *firmament* we understand the starry heaven, and if we understand it as being of the nature of the four elements, for the same reason it may be believed that the waters above the heaven are of the same nature as the elemental waters. But if by firmament we understand the starry heaven, not, however, as being of the nature of the four elements, then the waters above the firmament will not be of the same nature as the elemental waters. Rather just as, according to Strabo, one heaven is called empyrean, that is, fiery, solely because of its splendour, so this other heaven, which is above the starry heaven, will be called aqueous solely because of its transparence. Again, if the firmament is held to be of a nature other than the elements, it may still be said to divide the waters, if we understand by water not the element but formless matter. Augustine, in fact, says that whatever divides bodies from bodies can be said to divide waters from waters.

If, however, we understand by the firmament that part of the air in which the clouds are collected, then the waters above the firmament must rather be the vapors resolved from the waters which are raised above a part of the atmosphere, and from which the rain falls. But to say, as do some writers alluded to by Augustine, that waters resolved into vapor may be lifted above the starry heaven, is a mere absurdity. The solid nature of the firmament, the intervening region of fire, wherein all vapor must be consumed, the tendency in light and rarefied bodies to drift to one spot beneath the vault of the moon, as well as the fact that vapors are perceived not to rise even to the tops of the higher mountains – all go to show the impossibility of this. Nor it is less absurd to say, in support of this opinion, that bodies may be rarefied infinitely, since natural bodies cannot be infinitely rarefied or divided, but up to a certain point only.

16 Galileo's Unacknowledged Debt to his Predecessors, 1638

From *Two New Sciences*

THE THIRD DAY. – On equable (i.e., uniform) motion (*De motu aequabili*). In regard to equable or uniform (*uniformis*) motion, we have need of a single definition, which I give as follows. I understand by equal (*equalis*) or uniform movement one whose parts (*partes*) gone through (*peracte*) during any (*quibuscunque*) equal times are themselves equal. We must add to the old definition – which defined equable motion simply as one in which equal distances (*spatia*) are traversed in equal times – the word 'any' (quibuscumque), i.e., in 'all' (*omnibus*) equal periods of time . . . On movement naturally accelerated (*accelerato*) . . . If we examine the matter, we find no addition (*additamentum*) or increment (*incrementum*) more simple than that which always increases in the same way. This we readily understand when we consider the intimate relationship between time and motion; for just as equality, and uniformity, of motion is defined by, and conceived through, equalities of the time intervals and of spaces . . . so through the same equal periods of time we can conceive of increments of speed (*incrementa celeritatis*) simply added . . . To put the matter more clearly, if a moving body were to continue its motion with the same degree or moment of velocity (*gradus seu momentum velocitatis*) it acquired in the first time-interval, and continue to move uniformly with that degree of velocity, then its motion would be twice as slow as that which it would have if its velocity (*gradus celeritatis*) had been acquired in two time-intervals. And thus, it seems, we shall not be far wrong if we assume that increase in velocity (*intentio velocitatis*) is proportional to (*fieri iutxa*) the increase of time (*temporis extensio*).

COMMENTARY by M. Clagett

Anyone paying due attention to the Latin terminology of this passage will see how dependent Galileo still was on the Merton vocabulary. Thus *equalis motus, uniformis motus, gradus velocitatis,* and *intentio velocitatis* were all part of both vocabularies. Note once more that Galileo in this passage compared the instantaneous velocities at the end of the first time-period and at the end of the second time-period (in a uniformly accelerated movement) by imagining that the bodies were moving uniformly over some time-period with these respective instantaneous velocities. This as we have seen was precisely what Heytesbury and Swineshead recommended in their treatment of instantaneous velocity. Needless to add, also, the definitions of uniform velocity and uniform acceleration given by Galileo have their almost exact Merton counterparts.

The irrefutable proof that Galileo was familiar with the Merton vocabulary is given by a juvenile work, which bears the title *De Partibus sive grandibus qualitatis* (ed. Naz. Vol. I, 119–22). There we read (p. 120):

> It should be noted in the third place, that, since a quality is always in a quantitative subject, in addition to having proper (i.e. intensive) degress it also participates in a latitude of quantity and can be divided into quantitative parts. If the degrees or parts of the quality are compared throughout the parts of the quantity, either (1) the degrees of quality will be equal in any part at all and then the quality will be called 'uniform' or (2) the degrees will be unequal and then it will be called 'difform'. If the excesses of the parts will be equal so that in the first part there are two degrees, in the second part 4, in the third 6, and so on, so that the excess is always two, the quality will be called 'uniformly difform'. If however the excesses will be unequal, it will be called 'difformly difform'. Again if they will be unequal in such a way that

in the first part, for example, there will be 4 degrees, in the second 6, in the third 9, and so on, then the quality is called 'uniformly difformly difform'. If in truth the excesses will not be proportional, it will be called 'difformly difformly difform'.

It is of interest to note that Galileo's conception of uniformly difformly difform motion, if based on his use of the terms for qualities, would not be that of uniformly changing acceleration, but rather of an acceleration such that in succeeding equal periods of time the ratio of the velocity increments is some constant (other than I). This is the definition found in the *Tractatus de latitudinibus formarum*. This leads us to suspect that Galileo was familiar with this treatise, no doubt in one of its published editions.

Finally, we can remark that Galileo was much preoccupied with the whole problem of the intension and remission of forms and more than once he had occasion to write about it (cf. Ed. Naz., Vol. I, III–19, 133–57).

M. CLAGETT,

ed. *The Science of Mechanics in the Middle Ages*
pp. 251–2

17 Bacon's Criticisms of the Scholastics, 1605

From *The Advancement of Learning*

The second which followeth, is in nature worse than the former; for as substance of matter is better than beauty of words, so contrariwise vain matter is worse than vain words: wherein it seemeth the reprehension of St Paul was not only proper for those times, but prophetical for the times following; and not only respective to divinity, but extensive to all knowledge; *Devita profanas vocum novitates, et oppositiones falsi nominis scientiæ* (shun profane novelties of terms and oppositions of science falsely so called). For he assigneth two marks and badges of suspected and falsified science; the one, the novelty of and strangeness of terms; the other, the strictness of positions, which of necessity doth induce oppositions, and so questions and altercations. Surely, like as many substances in nature which are solid do putrefy and corrupt into worms, so it is the property of good and sound knowledge to putrefy and dissolve into a number of subtile, idle, unwholesome, and (as I may term them) vermiculate questions, which have indeed a kind of quickness and life of spirit, but no soundness of matter or goodness of quality. This kind of degenerate learning did chiefly reign amongst the schoolmen; who having sharp and strong wits, and abundance of leisure, and small variety of reading; but their wits being shut up in the cells of a few authors (chiefly Aristotle their dictator) as their persons were shut up in the cells of monasteries and colleges; and knowing little history, either of nature of time; did out of no great quantity of matter, and infinite agitation of wit, spin out unto us those laborious webs of learning which are extant in their books. For the wit and mind of man, if it work upon matter, which is the contemplation of the creatures of God, worketh according to the stuff, and is limited thereby; but if it work upon itself, as the spider worketh his web, then it is endless, and brings forth indeed cobwebs of learning, admirable for the fineness of thread and work, but of no substance or profit.

V

Social and Religious Considerations

The relative importance of theory and practice, pure science and technology, the scholar and the artisan, provides an issue upon which Marxists and non-Marxists hold divergent views. On the whole, in Marxist histories of science, we may expect a good deal of emphasis upon factors which may be broadly regarded as economic. For the non-Marxist historian, no such prediction can be made. In certain cases of scientific advance, technology may be seen to have been important, in others it may well have retarded progress. Artisans and craftsmen are not by definition tied to accepting improvements, indeed a successful tradition of practice may often lead them to oppose change. We may also expect Marxist historians to diminish the importance of scholars and of universities in the Scientific Revolution, whereas among non-Marxists there is a wide range of opinion on the matter. One of the reasons Francis Bacon tends to be a favourite figure with Marxist historians is because he expected the advancement of learning to come from the workshops and was critical of the universities. Kepler, on the other hand, tends to be ignored by them, because he was dominated by theoretical visions of no great practical consequence yet of the two there is no doubt that Kepler made an incomparably greater contribution to the advancement of learning.

The passages which follow illustrate these different points of view. Gabriel Harvey, a Cambridge don, praised the artisans in a passage much quoted by Marxists. The reader may well feel, however, that in its full context the compliment is something of a backhanded one. In contrast, Bishop Sprat, the historian of the Royal Society, criticized the conservatism of trades-men and thought that the free spirit of independent gentlemen was the best hope for the advancement of learning. Newton, in his turn, had some hard things to say about mechanics who lacked theoretical knowledge. Bacon criticized the universities but Sprat, though a Baconian in many respects, praised their contribution to science. Earlier, George Hakewill, another Baconian, had done much the same.

18 Faint Academic Praise for the Artisan? 1593

Gabriel Harvey (1545?–1630) fellow of Pembroke, Cambridge, was an arch controversialist of the late sixteenth century. His words are often quoted to indicate how the importance of artisans was acknowledged at the time but it is not clear whether in their full context, Harvey's praise of Humphrey Cole and his company is meant to be full-blooded.

From G. Harvey, *Pierce's Supererogation*

In the sovereign workmanship of Nature herself, what garden of flowers without weeds? What orchard of trees without worms? What field of corn without cockle? What pond of fishes without frogs? What sky of light without darkness? What mirror of knowledge without ignorance? What man of earth without frailty? What commodity of the world without discommodity? Oh! what an honourable and wonderful creature were perfection, were there any such visible creature under heaven? But pure Excellency dwelleth only above; and what mortal wisdom can acclear itself from error? or what heroical virtue can justify, I have no vice? The most precious things under the sun have their defaults; and the vilest things upon earth want not their graces. Virgil could enrich himself with the rubbish of Ennius: to how many rusty-dusty names was brave Livy beholding? Tully, that was as fine as the Crusado, disdained not some furniture of his predecessors, that were as coarse as canvas; and he that will diligently seek, may assuredly find treasure in marl, corn in straw, gold in dross, pearls in shell-fishes, precious stones in the dunghill of Esop, rich jewels of learning and wisdom in some poor boxes.

He that remembereth Humphrey Cole, a mathematical mechanician; Matthew Baker, a shipwright; John Shute, an architect; Robert Norman, a navigator; William Bourne, a gunner; John Hester, a chemist, or any like cunning and subtle empiric (Cole, Baker, Shute, Norman, Bourne, Hester, will be remembered when greater Clerks shall be forgotten), is a proud man if he contemn expert artizans, or any sensible industrious practitioner, howsoever unlectured in schools, or unlettered in books. Even the Lord Vulcan himself, the supposed god of the forge, and the thunder-smith of the great King Jupiter, took the repulse at the hands of the Lady Minerva, whom he would in ardent love have taken to wife. Yet what wit or policy honoureth not Vulcan? and what profound mathematician, like Digges, Harriot, or Dee, esteemeth not the pregnant mechanician? Let every man in his degree enjoy his due; and let the brave engineer, fine Dædalist, skilful Neptunist, marvellous Vulcanist, and every Mercurial occupationer, that is, every master of his craft, and every doctor of his mystery, be respected according to the uttermost extent of his public service, or private industry.

19 Sprat's Criticisms of Artisans, 1667

From *History of the Royal Society*

And indeed the Instances of this kind are so numerous, that I dare in general affirm, That those men who are not peculiarly conversant about any sort of Arts, may often find out their Rarities and Curiosities sooner, than those who have their minds confin'd wholly to them. If we weigh the Reasons why this is probable, it will not be found so much a paradox, as perhaps it seems at the first reading. The Tradesmen themselves having had their hands directed from their Youth in the same Methods of Working, cannot when they please so easily alter their custom, and turn themselves into new Rodes of Practice. Besides this, they chiefly labor for present livelyhood, and therefore cannot defer their Expectations so long, as is commonly requisit for the ripening of any new Contrivance. But especially having long handled their Instruments in the same fashion and regarded their Materials, with the same thoughts, they are not apt to be Surpriz'd much with them, nor to have any extraordinary Fancies, or Raptures about them.

These are usual defects of the Artificers themselves: Whereas the men of freer lives, have all the contrary advantages. They do not approach those Trades, as their dull, and unavoidable, and perpetual employments, but as their Diversions. They come to try those operations, in which they are not very exact, and so will be more frequently subject to commit errors in their proceeding: which very faults, and wandrings will often guid them into new light, and new Conceptions. And lastly there is also some privilege to be allow'd to the generosity of their spirits, which have not bin subdu'd, and clogg'd by any constant toyl, as the others. Invention is an Heroic thing, and plac'd above the reach of a low, and vulgar Genius. It requires an active, a bold, a nimble, a restless mind: a thousand difficulties must be contemn'd with which a mean heart would be broken: many attempts must be made to no purpose: much Treasure must sometimes be scatter'd without any return: much violence, and vigor of thoughts must attend it: some irregularities, and excesses must be granted it, that would hardly be pardon'd by the severe Rules of Prudence. All which may persuade us, that a large, and an unbounded mind is likely to be the Author of greater Productions, than the calm, obscure, and fetter'd indeavours of the Mechanics themselves: and that as in the Generation of Children, those are usually observ'd to be most sprightly, that are the stollen Fruits of an unlawful Bed; so in the Generations of the Brains those are often the most vigorous, and witty, which men beget on other Arts, and not on their own . . .

. . . Thus far I hope the way is cleer as I go: I have some confidence that I have sufficiently prov'd, that the Invention of Trades may still proceed farther, and that by the help of men of free lives, and by this cours of Experiments. But yet the main difficulty continues unremov'd. This arises from the suspicions of the Tradesmen themselves: They are generally infected with the narrowness that is natural to Corporations, which are wont to resist all new comers, as profess'd Enemies to their Privileges: And by these interested men it may be objected, That the growth of new Inventions and new Artificers, will infallibly reduce all the old ones to poverty and decay.

20 Newton and the Gunners, 1681

From his *Correspondence*, ed. G. H. Turnbull, ii. 360.

The instance of a bullet shot out of a cannon and keeping the same side forward may be a tradition of the Gunners, but I do not see how it can consist with the laws of motion, and therefore dare venture to say that upon a fair trial, 'twill not succeed excepting sometimes by accident. The trial may thus be made. Upon a spell or bridge such as school boys play with, lay a large ball one hemisphere of which is white the other black. Either hemisphere lying upwards, strike the end of the bridge to make the ball rise and if the ball receive not any circulating motion from the stroke you will see that hemisphere which is laid upwards continue upwards as well falling as rising. If I did not know the event of the experiment by the reason of it, yet I could guess at it by what I have observed of a hand ball tossed up.

21 Bacon and the Universities, 1620

From *The New Organon*

Again, in the customs and institutions of schools, academies, colleges, and similar bodies destined for the abode of learned men and the cultivation of learning, everything is found adverse to the progress of science. For the lectures and exercises there are so ordered, that to think or speculate on anything out of the common way can hardly occur to any man. And if one or two have the boldness to use any liberty of judgement, they must undertake the task all by themselves; they can have no advantage from the company of others. And if they can endure this also, they will find their industry and largeness of mind no slight hindrance to their fortune. For the studies of men in these places are confined and as it were imprisoned in the writings of certain authors, from whom if any man dissent he is straightway arraigned as a turbulent person and an innovator. But surely there is a great distinction between matters of state and the arts; for the danger from the new motion and from the new light is not the same. In matters of state a change even for the better is distrusted, because it unsettles what is established; these things resting on authority, consent, fame and opinion, not on demonstration. But arts and sciences should be like mines, where the noise of new works and further advances is heard on every side. But though the matter be so according to right reason, it is not so acted on in practice; and the points above mentioned in the administration and government of learning put a severe restraint upon the advancement of the sciences.

22 Hakewill's Praise of Oxford, 1627

George Hakewill (1578–1649) was a fellow and later rector of Exeter College, Oxford. In the seventeenth-century controversy between Ancients and Moderns, he was among the first Englishmen publicly to take the Modern side.

From *Apologie . . . of the Power and Providence of God.*

Were I destitute of all other arguments to demonstrate the providence of God, in the preservation of the world, and to prove that it doth not universally and perpetually decline, this one might suffice for all, that though, my Venerable Mother though thou wax old in regard of years, yet in this latter age in regard of strength and beauty, waxest young again. Within the compass of this last centenarie and less, though thou hast brought forth such a number of worthy sons, for piety, for learning, for wisdom and for buildings hast been so enlarged and enriched, that hee who shall compare thee with thyself will easily finde, that though thou bee truly accounted one of the most ancient universities in the world, yet so farre art thou from withering and wrinkles, that thou art rather become fairer and fresher in thine issue no less happy than heretofore.

23 Sprat's Defence of the Universities, 1667

From *History of the Royal Society*

By this discours, I hope, I have said enough, to manifest the innocence of this Design in respect of all the present Schools of Learning; and especially our own Universities. And it was but just that we should have this tenderness, for the Interest of those magnificent seats of humane Knowledge, and divine; to which the Natural Philosophy of our Nation, cannot be injurious without horrible ingratitude; seeing in them it has been principally cherish'd, and reviv'd. From thence the greatest part of our Modern Inventions have deduc'd their Original. It is true such Experimental Studies are largely dispers'd at this time: But they first came forth thence, as the Colonies of old did from Rome: and therefore as those did, they should rather intend the strength, than the destruction of their Mother-Cities.

24 Sprat's Anti-Puritanism, 1667

From *History of the Royal Society*

It was therefore, some space after the end of the Civil Wars at Oxford, in Dr. Wilkins his Lodgings, in Wadham College, which was then the place of Resort for Vertuous, and Learned Men, that the first meetings were made, which laid the foundation of all this that follow'd. The

University had, at that time, many Members of its own, who had begun a free way of reasoning; and was also frequented by some Gentlemen, of Philosophical Minds, whom the misfortunes of the Kingdom, and the security and ease of a retirement amongst Gownmen, had drawn thither.

Their first purpose was no more, then only the satisfaction of breathing a freer air, and of conversing in quiet one with another, without being ingag'd in the passions, and madness of that dismal Age. And from the Institution of that Assembly, it had been enough, if no other advantage had come, but this: That by this means there was a race of young Men provided, against the next Age, whose minds receiving them, their first Impressions of sober and generous knowledge, were invincibly arm'd against all the enchantments of Enthusiasm. But what is more, I may venture to affirm, that it was in good measure by the influence, which these Gentlemen had over the rest, that the University itself, or at least, any part of its Discipline, and Order, was sav'd from ruine. And from hence we may conclude, that the same Men have now no intention, of sweeping away all the honor of Antiquity in this their new Design: seeing they imploy'd so much of their labor, and prudence, in preserving that most venerable seat of ancient Learning, when their shrinking from its defence, would have been the speediest way to have destroy'd it. For the Truth of this, I dare appeal to all uninterested men, who knew the Temper of that place; and especially to those who were my own contemporaries there: of whom I can name very many, whom the happy restoration of the Kingdom's peace, found as well inclin'd, to serve their Prince, and the Church, as if they had been bred up in the most prosperous condition of their Country. This was undoubtedly so. Nor indeed could it be otherwise: for such Spiritual Frenzies, which did then bear Rule, can never stand long, before a cleer, and a deep skill in Nature. It is almost impossible, that they, who converse much with the subtilty of things, should be deluded by such thick deceits. There is but one better charm in the world, then Real Philosophy, to allay the impulses of the false spirit: and that is, the blessed presence, and assistance of the True.

25 Sprat and the Contribution of England, 1667

From *History of the Royal Society*

They have therefore been most rigorous in putting in execution, the only Remedy, that can be found for this extravagance: and that has been a constant Resolution, to reject all the amplifications, digressions, and swelling of style: to return back to the primitive purity, and short-ness when men deliver'd so many things, almost in an equal number of words. They have exacted from all their members, a close, naked, natural way of speaking; positive expressions; clear senses; a native easiness: bringing all things as near the Mathematical plainness, as they can: and preferring the language of Artizans, Countrymen, and Merchants, before that of Wits, or Scholars.

And here, there is one thing, not to be pass'd by; which will render this establish'd custom of the society, well-nigh everlasting: and that is, the general constitution of the minds of the English. I have already often insisted on some of the prerogatives of England; wherebye it may justly lay claim, to be the Head of a Philosophical league, above all other Countries in Europe: I have urg'd its situation, its present Genius, and the disposition of its Merchants; and many more such arguments to incourage us, still remain to be us'd: But of all others, this, which I am now alledging, is of the most weighty, and important consideration. If there can be a true character given of the Universal Temper of any Nation under Heaven: then certainly this must be ascrib'd to our Countrymen: that they have commonly an unaffected sincerity; that they love to deliver their minds with a sound simplicity; that they have the middle qualities, between the reserv'd subtle southern, and the rough unhewn Northern people: that they are not extreamly prone to speak: that they are more concern'd, what others will think of the strength, than of the fineness of what they say: and that an universal modesty possesses them. These Qualities are so conspic-uous, and proper to our Soil; that we often hear them objected to us, by some of our neighbour Satyrists, in more disgraceful expressions. For they are wont to revile the English, with a want of familiarity; with a melancholy dumpishness; with slowness, silence, and with the unrefin'd sullenness of their behaviour. But these are only the re-proaches of partiality or ignorance: for they ought rather to neglect of circumstances and flourishes; for regarding things of greater moment, more than less; for a scorn to deceive as well as to be deceiv'd: which are all the best indowments, that can enter into a Philosophical Mind. So that even the position of our climate, the air, the influence of the heaven, the composition of the English blood; as well as the embraces of the Ocean, seem to joyn with the labours of the Royal Society, to render our Country, a Land of Experimental knowledge. And it is a good sign, that Nature will reveal more of its secrets to the English, than to others; because it has already furnished them with a Genius so well proportion'd for the receiving, and retaining its mysteries.

26 Scepticism About Science, c. 1700

Jonathan Swift (1667–1745), among his many other literary activities, took part in the seventeenth-century controversy between Ancients and Moderns. His sympathies lay on the side of the Ancients and as these passages reveal he was bitterly hostile to the pretensions of the academies and the 'new philosophy'.

From *Gulliver's Travels*

(I)

This Academy is not an entire single Building, but a Continuation of several Houses on both Sides of a Street; which growing waste, was purchased and applyed to that Use.

I was received very kindly by the Warden, and went for many Days to the Academy. Every Room hath in it one or more Projectors; and I believe I could not be in fewer than five Hundred Rooms.

The first Man I saw was of a meagre Aspect, with sooty Hands and Face, his Hair and Beard long, ragged and singed in several Places. His Clothes, Shirt, and Skin were all of the same Colour. He had been Eight Years upon a Project for extracting Sun-Beams out of Cucumbers, which were to be put into Vials hermetically sealed, and let out to warm the Air in raw inclement Summers. He told me, he did not doubt in Eight Years more, that he should be able to supply the Governors Gardens with Sun-shine at a reasonable Rate; but he complained that his Stock was low, and intreated me to give him something as an Encouragement to Ingenuity, especially since this had been a very dear Season for Cucumbers. I made him a small Present, for my Lord had furnished me with Money on purpose, because he knew their Practice of begging from all who go to see them.

(II)

I then desired the Governor to call up *Descartes* and *Gassendi*, with whom I prevailed to explain their Systems to *Aristotle*. This great Philosopher freely acknowledged his own Mistakes in Natural Philosophy, because he proceeded in many things upon Conjecture, as all Men must do; and he found, that *Gassendi*, who had made the Doctrine of *Epicurus* as palatable as he could, and the *Vortices* of *Descartes*, were equally exploded. He predicted the same Fate to *Attraction*, whereof the present Learned are such zealous Asserters. He said, that new Systems of Nature were but new Fashions, which would vary in every Age; and even those who pretend to demonstrate them from Mathematical Principles, would flourish but a short Period of Time, and be out of Vogue when that was determined.

[See also p. 132 for Lorkes views].

Part Three
SOME PERSPECTIVES CONSIDERED

Further
Scientific Revolutions?

By the mid-twentieth century, the achievement of Copernicus, Galileo and Newton no longer seems to constitute a unique Scientific Revolution, without parallel in human history. There are strong grounds for considering the claims of ancient China and of ancient Greece to have experienced scientific movements which may be regarded not unfairly as revolutions. But more significant still are the developments in Europe which have taken place since Newton's day and which suggest that other Scientific Revolutions have occurred. Newtonian science, by which is meant both the work of Newton himself and of those who successfully applied similar methods in the eighteenth and early nineteenth centuries, explained the natural universe by means of a limited vocabulary of terms. As observation intensified and the field of exploration widened, it gradually became clear that this vocabulary was insufficiently flexible to deal with the great stream of new phenomena in which scientists were interested. Newton, for example, had believed that matter was composed of innumerable, indestructible atoms, a hypothesis which the work of Dalton and others around the year 1800 apparently proved beyond argument. By 1900, a new sub-atomic world was coming into focus, with rules and paradoxes exclusively its own. The Galileo of this scientific revolution was a Scotsman, Clerk Maxwell, its Padua was the Cavendish laboratory at Cambridge and its Kepler was Albert Einstein. Among the others who were associated with the revolution were Rayleigh, Rutherford, Bohr, Schrödinger and Heisenburg. A new world of sub-atomic particles now occupied the centre of attention, in which the laws of Newton no longer seemed to apply.

The details of this revolution, like those of any pursuit which employs a technical vocabulary, tend to repel the non-scientific observer. Nevertheless, it is possible to study the movement, in part at least, from an historical point of view, using as a standard of comparison the first Scientific Revolution and the points which historians have made in connection with it.

The role of the universities in each movement, for example, invites discussion at an historical level. Whatever view one takes of the importance of the universities in the first scientific revolution, the pre-eminence of the universities in the second seems unmistakable. But it is not clear why particular universities such as Cambridge and Göttingen came to the fore while other, equally illustrious, foundations remained in the background. The reasons for this situation may lie in tradition, in the influence of particular individuals, in government policy, in private endowment or in other causes. But the answer is not immediately self-evident and can be reached only by answering specific historical questions. In the course of this investigation, the importance of non-academic institutions would need to be examined. There were a number of scientists, Michael Faraday, for example, who had no formal higher education and yet were able to make an original contribution to scientific research. If the work of individuals like Faraday and of non-university institutes turn out to be of greater significance than expected, this would lead us to revise our opinions about the type of environment in which original scientific work may be expected to flourish. And looking back to the seventeenth century, it would lead us to re-examine the part played by artisans and craftsmen. The fixed curriculum of universities and the heavy teaching load borne by academics may militate in the long run against scientific achievement.

In the second scientific revolution, as in the first, the problem of different national contributions cannot be ignored. In many textbooks, there is an understandable tendency to refer many problems to national stereotypes, English rule of thumb, French logic-chopping, and German mysticism. G. C. Gillispie, for example in his masterly book *The Edge of Objectivity* cannot refrain from referring to 'the provincial universalism of French learning'. If we contrast individuals in a simple way there may be something to be said for using the notion of national differences in this manner. But the real problem, at a serious level, is the extent to which national educational traditions operate in such a way as to produce distinctively national modes of thought. If men think on different lines the questions they ask will be different. The divergence between English and continental schools of mathematics during the eighteenth and nineteenth centuries may be taken as a classical example of different national approaches. This cleavage went back ultimately to a conflict of opinion, on more than one matter, between Newton and Leibniz and its long-term results may well have been profound in cutting off England from full appreciation of continental research.

The same kind of difference may be seen in the French refusal to accept the Darwinian theory of evolution. In this, as in so many other spheres, it was considered that matters were ordered better in France. It may not be unduly paradoxical to regard French science at different periods as being different from English science. But the problem which this raises can be solved only by going beyond the easy solution of national stereotypes and looking in an historical way at the systems of education in various countries.

The problem here is not confined to Western Europe. It also includes the United States and Russia which, for apparently different reasons, produced many fewer scientists, in relation to their population at this time, than European countries generally. In attempting to explain this, we are led once more to an important historical problem. In the United States, the weakness of scientific research during the period of the second scientific revolution may have been due to the strength of big business, and the resulting emphasis upon technical know-how and material considerations. If this is true, it would be another reason for criticizing the Marxist view of the relationship between pure science and technology. In Russia, on the other hand, one of the reasons why science did not flourish was the influence of the Slavophiles, who were opposed to science and all similar manifestations of Western culture. Thus to examine the fate of science in these two countries leads the student at once into the main stream of social history.

The relationship between industrialization and science is clearly a problem of major importance. The evidence suggests that some measure of industrialization is an essential condition of scientific advance but not a certain ingredient for success. It would be of great interest to pin down how the world of the industrial revolution influenced the scientist and perhaps the answer in all cases might not be as expected. Clerk Maxwell wrote, later in his life, 'I find I get fonder of metaphysics and less of calculation and my metaphysics are fast settling down in that rigid high style that is about ten times above Whewell as Mill is below him and Macaulay below him'. It may be argued that the second scientific revolution represented a reaction against the mechanism of the world of nineteenth-century industrialism. Here again a wider perspective comes into view.

The relationship between government patronage of science and the second scientific revolution may also claim our attention. National traditions in this field have varied a good deal. In France since Napoleon's day and before, government sponsorship of science has been taken for granted. In England until recent decades there has been little direct government aid for scientific research. The situation has now been reached in most countries where government help is accepted as a matter of course, for the reason that the scale of science has outgrown the framework of private benefaction. The course of events in both the first and second scientific revolutions may lead us to wonder whether this is the kind of development which will lead to humdrum tradition in which governments get the results for which they pay and nothing more. This is quite distinct from the problem of undue political influence upon scientists in both totalitarian and non-totalitarian countries. Study of the way in which scientific discoveries were made during the second scientific revolution may lead us to the conclusion that the uncovenanted spark of inspiration is most likely to fall in places where the administrative mind has no foothold.

There remains the question of religion. It has been maintained by many historians that Protestantism in its various forms acted as a powerful motive force in inducing men to take up the scientific observation of nature. Can the same be said about the second scientific revolution? It is true that Faraday was a member of the obscure sect of Sandemanians, whose anti-intellectual tenets may well have provided the source of his own deep dislike of speculation in scientific matters. But one dissenter does not make a conventicle, and before the problem is resolved the religious views of many scientists will need to be examined. During the first scientific revolution itself it is by no means clear that the great scientists were protestant in the usual sense of the word. There is good evidence for thinking that the religious beliefs of Galileo, Kepler, Descartes, Boyle, Harvey and Newton fell into no strict category of orthodoxy, either Catholic or Protestant.

One further point may be made. It has been suggested recently that the present relationship between theory and fact in physics is one of uneasy compromise. New facts are discovered and as a consequence new patches are made in the accepted pattern. These are the modern equivalent of the epicycles and eccentrics by means of which the practical astronomers once succeeded in reconciling their own observations of planetary motion with the Ptolemaic theory. This unstable intellectual equilibrium may lead some to expect that a new synthesis is on the point of being produced by a simple process of accumulation, as a crystal will change a super-saturated solution. But the Ptolemaic compromise lasted for well over a millennium. If the conditions are turning against scientific advance, our own Ptolemaic age may last equally as long.

As a postscript, it may be suggested that a Third Scientific Revolution also took place in the nineteenth century, distinct in every feature from what was taking place in the world of Faraday and Clerk Maxwell. Whereas the Atomic Revolution was largely concerned with space. The nineteenth century also witnessed an equally radical revolution in its approach to time. By 1700 space had taken its place in scientific explanation, but the universe was still conceived of as a comparatively recent creation. Only in the nineteenth century was a time scale conceived of which made it possible for men to consider evolutionary hypotheses. First the age of the world, then of man and finally the age of the universe came to be regarded in a new historical dimension. This revolution in men's approach to the universe was as significant in its own way as the Mathematical Revolution of the seventeenth century. Its importance may be overlooked however, because its impact upon the material conditions of our society has been so much less. The theory of evolution stands as one of the supreme examples of scientific understanding without any practical application. Why Darwin was able to take such imaginative steps at this time raises similar historical problems to those involved in the achievements of Galileo.

Further Reading

General

S. TOULMIN. *Foresight and Understanding*. Hutchinson, 1961.

J. H. RANDALL. *The Career of Philosophy*. Oxford U.P., 1962.

M. CLAGETT, ed. *Critical Problems in the History of Science*. Univ. of Wisconsin Press, 1959.

B. BARBER and W. HIRSCH. *The Sociology of Science*. Macmillan, 1962.

General Surveys

G. C. GILLISPIE. *The Edge of Objectivity*. Princeton U.P., 1960.

H. BUTTERFIELD. *Origins of Modern Science*. Bell, 1950.

S. TOULMIN and J. GOODFIELD. *The Architecture of Matter*. Hutchinson, 1962.

E. J. DIJKSTERHUIS. *The Mechanisation of the World Picture*. Oxford U.P., 1961.

Greek Science

S. SAMBURSKY. *The Physical World of the Greeks*. Routledge (paperback), 1962.

Medieval Science

M. CLAGETT, ed. *The Science of Mechanics in the Middle Ages*. Univ. of Wisconsin Press, 1959.

A. C. CROMBIE. *Robert Grosseteste and the Origins of Experimental Science*. Oxford U.P., 1953.

The Sixteenth and Seventeenth Centuries

W. P. D. WIGHTMAN. *Science and the Renaissance*. Oliver and Boyd, 1962.

A. R. HALL. *The Scientific Revolution*. Longmans, 1954.

A. KOYRÉ. *From Closed Space to Infinite Universe*. Harper Torchbooks, 1958.

I. B. COHEN. *The Birth of a New Physics*. Heinemann, 1961.

The Eighteenth and Nineteenth Centuries

L. EISELEY. *Darwin's Century*. Gollancz, 1958.

G. C. GILLISPIE. *Genesis and Geology*. Harper Torchbooks, 1959; and relevant chapters in *The Edge of Objectivity*.

The Twentieth Century

A. EINSTEIN and L. INFELD. *The Evolution of Physics*. Cambridge U.P., 1961.

Index